CONTENTS

D1501096

GRADE **4**

UNIT 1 · GRAMMAR

Sentences

What Is a Sentence?	1
Declarative and Interrogative Sentences	2
Imperative and Exclamatory Sentences	3
Complete Subjects and Complete Predicates	4
Simple Subjects	5
Simple Predicates	6
Compound Subjects and Compound Predicates	7
Correcting Run-on Sentences	8
Mechanics: Punctuating Sentences	9
Vocabulary Building: Using Context Clues	10
Grammar and Writing Connection: Combining Sentences	11

UNIT 2 · WRITING

Writing Personal Narratives

Group Writing: A Personal Narrative	12
Thinking and Writing: Main Idea and Details	13
Writer's Resources: The Dictionary	14
Writer's Resources: Dictionary Entries	15

UNIT 3 · GRAMMAR

Nouns

What Is a Noun?	16
Singular Nouns and Plural Nouns	17
More Singular Nouns and Plural Nouns	18
More Plural Nouns	19
Common Nouns and Proper Nouns	20
Singular Possessive Nouns	21
Plural Possessive Nouns	22
Using Possessive Nouns	23
Mechanics: Abbreviations	24
Vocabulary Building: Compound Words	25
Grammar and Writing Connection: Combining Sentences	26

UNIT 4 · WRITING
Writing Explanations
Group Writing: An Explanation	27
Thinking and Writing: Comparing and Contrasting	28
Writer's Resources: The Library	29
Writer's Resources: The Card Catalog	30

UNIT 5 · GRAMMAR
Action Verbs
What Is an Action Verb?	31
Main Verbs and Helping Verbs	32
Verb Tenses	33
More About Verb Tenses	34
Subject-Verb Agreement	35
Using Irregular Verbs I	36
Using Irregular Verbs II	37
Spelling Verbs Correctly	38
Mechanics: Using the Comma	39
Vocabulary Building: Prefixes	40
Grammar and Writing Connection: Making Subjects and Verbs Agree	41

UNIT 6 · WRITING
Writing Letters
Group Writing: A Friendly Letter	42
Thinking and Writing: Solving Problems	43
Writer's Resources: Parts of a Book	44

UNIT 7 · GRAMMAR
Linking Verbs
What Is a Linking Verb?	45
Linking Verbs in the Present Tense	46
Linking Verbs in the Past Tense	47
Using Linking Verbs	48
Contractions with *not*	49
Mechanics: Using Quotation Marks	50
Vocabulary Building: Suffixes	51
Grammar and Writing Connection: Combining Sentences	52

UNIT 8 · WRITING
Writing Stories

Group Writing: A Story 53
Thinking and Writing: Understanding Sequence 54
Writer's Resources: The Thesaurus 55

UNIT 9 · GRAMMAR
Adjectives

What Is an Adjective? 56
Adjectives After Linking Verbs 57
Adjectives That Compare 58
Spelling Adjectives That Compare 59
Comparing with more and most 60
Using Articles 61
Mechanics: Capitalizing Proper Adjectives 62
Vocabulary Building: Synonyms and Antonyms 63
Grammar and Writing Connection: Choosing Vivid
  Adjectives 64

UNIT 10 · WRITING
Writing Descriptions

Group Writing: A Description 65
Thinking and Writing: Classifying Sensory Details 66
Writer's Resources: The Encyclopedia 67

UNIT 11 · GRAMMAR
Pronouns

What Is a Pronoun? 68
Subject Pronouns 69
Object Pronouns 70
Possessive Pronouns 71
Using I and me Correctly 72
Mechanics: Pronoun Contractions 73
Vocabulary Building: Homophones and Homographs 74
Grammar and Writing Connection: Combining Sentences 75

UNIT 12 · WRITING
Writing Persuasive Paragraphs

Group Writing: A Persuasive Paragraph   76
Thinking and Writing: Telling Fact from Opinion   77
Writer's Resources: The Atlas and the Almanac   78

UNIT 13 · GRAMMAR
Adverbs

What Is an Adverb?   79
More About Adverbs   80
Using Adverbs to Compare   81
Using *good* and *well* Correctly   82
Negatives   83
Mechanics: Punctuating Titles   84
Vocabulary Building: Borrowed Words   85
Grammar and Writing Connection: Combining Sentences   86

UNIT 14 · WRITING
Writing Research Reports

Group Writing: A Research Report   87
Thinking and Writing: Summarizing   88
Writer's Resources: Graphs, Tables, and Maps   89

Answers   T1–T45

What Is a Sentence?

A **sentence** is a group of words that expresses a complete thought.

ASK   Does the group of words express a complete thought?
       Does it tell about a person or thing and what the person or
       thing did?

If the answer to both questions is *yes*, then the group of words is a
sentence. If the answer is *no*, then the group of words is not a sentence.

Patsy's cat ran up a tree. = a sentence
Up a tree. = not a sentence

A. Underline each sentence.

1. One day Patsy couldn't find
her cat.
Couldn't find her cat.

2. Called and called for him.
Patsy called and called for him.

3. She looked under the porch.
Under the porch.

4. Soon the sky would get dark.
Soon the sky.

5. Got very worried.
Patsy got very worried.

6. Sometimes the cat.
Sometimes the cat goes to
the park.

7. Patsy walked through the park.
Through the park.

8. A small meow.
She heard a small meow.

9. The sound came from a tree.
Came from a tree.

10. Her cat was on the top branch.
On the top branch.

B. Write whether each group of words is or is not a **sentence.**

11. Ran to a telephone. _____

12. Patsy called the fire department. _____

13. The fire truck raced down the street. _____

14. Noise of the fire truck. _____

15. The cat ran down the tree. _____

Name

Declarative and Interrogative Sentences

A declarative sentence
makes a statement. ——————→ Insects have six legs.
An interrogative sentence
asks a question. ——————→ Do insects have six legs?

A. Underline each sentence that tells something.

1. Insects have three parts to their bodies.
2. They also have feelers and wings.
3. Are spiders insects?
4. Spiders have eight legs and no wings.
5. Do spiders have two or three parts to their bodies?

B. Underline each sentence that asks something.

6. A fly is an insect.
7. Can flies walk upside down?
8. Do flies smell with their feelers?
9. How fast do the wings of a fly move?
10. A fly's wings beat about 200 times a minute.

C. Follow the directions.

11. Write a sentence that tells something about an insect. Put a period at the end of your sentence.

_____

12. Write a sentence that asks something about an insect. Put a question mark at the end of your sentence.

_____

Name

Imperative and Exclamatory Sentences

An **imperative sentence** can tell or ask
someone to do something. ————————→ Cut the meat.
An **exclamatory sentence** can show
strong feeling. ————————————→ What lean meat this is!

A. Underline each sentence that tells or asks someone to do something.

1. Wash the vegetables carefully.
2. How hot the water is!
3. Peel the potatoes.
4. Throw the skins in the garbage can.
5. That garbage can smells bad!

B. Underline each sentence that shows strong feeling.

6. Quick, the water is boiling over!
7. Turn the heat down.
8. Put the potatoes into the water.
9. Cook the potatoes for about 20 minutes.
10. What a delicious stew you made!

C. Follow the directions.

11. Write a sentence that tells or asks someone to do something about cooking. Put a period at the end of your sentence.

12. Write a sentence that shows strong feeling about cooking. Put an exclamation point at the end of your sentence.

Name _____

Complete Subjects and Complete Predicates

A **complete subject,** or subject part, ⟶ includes all the words that tell whom or what the sentence is about.

A **complete predicate,** or predicate part, ⟶ includes all the words that tell what the subject does or is.

Read this sentence.   My family   goes to the park.

⎣____⎦ complete subject   ⎣_____⎦ complete predicate

A. Finish each sentence with a complete subject from the box.

**All ants   Some children   A few dogs
Colorful flowers   Two squirrels**

---

1. _____ look for nuts to eat.

2. _____ have two antennae.

3. _____ ride bicycles.

4. _____ bloom in a garden.

5. _____ bark loudly.

B. Finish each sentence with a complete predicate from the box.

**blows through the trees   flies his kite   rocks her baby
swim in the pond   eats a big worm**

---

6. Some fish _____ .

7. A little boy _____ .

8. A mother _____ .

9. A robin _____ .

10. A warm breeze _____ .

Name

Simple Subjects

The **complete subject** includes all the words that tell whom or what
the sentence is about.

My mother   gave my sister a birthday party.

The **simple subject** is the main word or group of words in the
complete subject.

A. Underline the complete subject. Then write the simple subject.

1. Many children came to the party.   _____

2. Colorful balloons were everywhere.   _____

3. Many presents sat beside a chair.   _____

4. One large box was covered with blue paper. _____

5. My sister opened the presents.   _____

B. Circle the simple subject.

6. Our next-door neighbor gave her a book.

7. A silly clown jumped out of one box.

8. The children laughed with surprise.

9. Our grey cat played in the wrapping paper.

10. My parents took pictures at the party.

C. Complete each sentence with a simple subject that makes sense.

11. My _____ made the food for the party.

12. The _____ tasted delicious.

13. The _____ at the party ate all the food.

14. Our little _____ gobbled up the crumbs on the floor.

15. All the _____ left the party at five o'clock.

Simple Predicates

> The **complete predicate** includes all the words that tell what the subject does or is.
>
> My class | took a trip to a fire station.
>
> The **simple predicate** is the main word or group of words in the complete predicate.

A. Underline the complete predicate. Then write the simple predicate.

1. The chief meets us at the door. _____

2. The children walk inside the station. _____

3. Some fire fighters eat their breakfasts. _____

4. Other fire fighters polish a fire engine. _____

5. The children talk to the fire fighters. _____

B. Circle each simple predicate.

6. A young dog runs around the station.

7. The fire fighters named him Rex.

8. Rex barks loudly sometimes.

9. The children love Rex.

10. The black and white dog lives at the fire station.

C. Complete each sentence with a simple predicate that makes sense.

11. The alarm _____ very loudly.

12. The fire fighters _____ to the fire engine.

13. The doors of the fire station _____ quickly.

14. The fire engines _____ down the street.

15. The children _____ the fire engines.

Name

Compound Subjects and Compound Predicates

A **compound subject** is two or more simple subjects that have the same predicate. The simple subjects are joined by **and.**

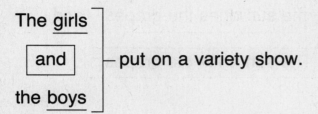

A **compound predicate** is two or more simple predicates that have the same subject. The simple predicates are joined by **and.**

Katie — plays the piano

and

sings a song.

A. Underline the compound subject in each sentence.

1. Linda and Kelly sing a duet.
2. My sister and brother perform bicycle tricks.
3. My good friend and her neighbor dance with taps on their shoes.
4. My teacher and her husband play trumpets.
5. My family and friends sit in the audience.

B. Underline the compound predicate in each sentence.

6. Mr. Davis fixes and works the lights.
7. Dad rents and borrows some chairs.
8. Other helpers cook and serve refreshments.
9. The performers smile and bow at the end of the show.
10. The audience claps and cheers.

Name

Correcting Run-on Sentences

A **run-on sentence** contains two or more sentences that run together.

To fix a run-on sentence, break it into shorter sentences.

People grow grapes   and   the sun dries the grapes   and

| People grow grapes. | | The sun dries the grapes. |

they become raisins.

| They become raisins. |

Fix each run-on sentence by breaking it into shorter sentences. Write
the new sentences on the lines.

1. Many people grow grapes and some growers live in California and some
live in other warm places in the world.

_____

_____

2. A farmer raises grapes in a vineyard and the grapes hang on a vine and
they grow in bunches.

_____

_____

3. Then workers pick the grapes and they put the grapes on wooden trays
and the sun shines on the grapes for many days.

_____

_____

4. The grapes become wrinkled and their green color turns to a blackish
brown and finally they are raisins.

_____

_____

Mechanics: Punctuating Sentences

Every sentence must begin with a capital letter.

A **declarative** sentence makes a statement or tells something.

  It ends with a period. ⟶ A boat ride is fun.

An **imperative** sentence tells or asks someone to do something.

  It ends with a period. ⟶ Don't drop the oars.

An **interrogative** sentence asks something.

  It ends with a question mark. ⟶ Do you like boat rides?

An **exclamatory** sentence shows strong feeling.

  It ends with an exclamation point. ⟶ Boat rides are exciting!

Write each sentence correctly. Add a capital letter and the correct end punctuation.

1. this boat is a canoe

_____

2. don't rock the canoe

_____

3. why must we be so careful

_____

4. a canoe can tip over easily

_____

5. should I paddle like this

_____

6. stop, we're heading for those rocks

_____

Name _____

Vocabulary Building:
Using Context Clues

Context clues are the words that come before and after an unfamiliar word in a sentence.

The context clues in the following sentence can help you understand the meaning of the word *descends.*

A waterfall is a stream that <u>descends</u> suddenly from a higher level to a lower level.

The words *from a higher level to a lower level* tell you that *descends* means "goes down."

Read each sentence and look for context clues. Then write the correct meaning of each underlined word.

1. The water in some waterfalls <u>plunges</u> hundreds of feet to the bottom.

falls quickly   flows upward   _____

2. Other waterfalls are not very high, but their <u>breadth</u> is great.

height   width   _____

3. If the <u>volume</u> of water in a waterfall is small, there is not enough water to produce electricity.

temperature   amount   _____

4. The <u>immense</u> size of some waterfalls creates breathtaking scenery.

large   small   _____

5. Angels Falls, the world's highest falls, crash straight down, <u>uninterrupted</u> by rocks.

stopped briefly   without being stopped   _____

6. In 1935, James Angel was the first American to <u>espy</u> the Angels Falls with his own eyes.

see   name   _____

Grammar and Writing Connection: Combining Sentences

Use the words **and** or **but** to connect two sentences.
And means "in addition."

| All birds have wings. | + | Most birds can fly. |

All birds have wings, **and** most birds can fly.

But shows a contrast.

| Ostriches cannot fly. | + | They can run very fast. |

Ostriches cannot fly, **but** they can run very fast.

Remember to put a comma before the joining word.

Combine each pair of sentences. Use the word in parentheses to join the sentences.

1. Some birds fly at night. Others fly during the day.   (but)

_____

_____

2. The hummingbird is the smallest bird. The ostrich is the largest bird.   (and)

_____

_____

3. Birds sit on their eggs. The heat makes the chicks grow.   (and)

_____

_____

4. Some small birds live on seeds. Hawks eat rabbits and snakes.   (but)

_____

_____

Name

Group Writing: A Personal Narrative

- A **personal narrative** tells something about what has happened to the writer.
- A personal narrative should have an **interesting beginning sentence** which tells the **main idea.**
- A personal narrative also contains **detail sentences** which support, or say more about, the main idea.
- A personal narrative should be written in **time order.** When a personal narrative is written in time order, the events are told in the order in which they actually happened.

Time order	First event ⟶ I jumped into the pool.
	Second event ⟶ I swam for an hour.
	Third event ⟶ I dried off in the sun.

Read the following personal narratives. Then list the details from each narrative in the correct time order.

1. I was so excited about using my new roller skates, that I could hardly wait to bring them home! The first thing I did was to strap them on my feet. Then I skated down the sidewalk. I was skating well, until I suddenly lost my balance and fell.

   First event: _____

   Second event: _____

   Third event: _____

2. I wanted to send my grandmother something special. First, I got some paper, scissors, and colored pencils. Then, I spent the afternoon making her a beautiful card. Finally, I wrote her a letter inside the card.

   First event: _____

   Second event: _____

   Third event: _____

Name

Thinking and Writing:
Main Idea and Details

- A personal narrative has a **main idea.** It can be the beginning sentence. It tells what the narrative will be about.
- The other sentences in the narrative are **detail sentences.** They support the main idea, or tell more information about it.

main idea sentence ⟶ I'll never forget the time I marched in a Memorial Day Parade.

detail sentences ⟶ I wore my cub scout uniform.
I carried a flag.
I had sore feet the next day.

Read the paragraph. On the lines below, write the main idea sentence and the three detail sentences that support it. Put a line through the sentence in the paragraph that does not support the main idea.

Helping My Neighbor

Because my neighbor is recovering from an illness, I help her with her chores. Every Friday I shop for her at the grocery store. Sometimes I go to the post office for her. Yesterday, I raked the leaves in her yard. Tomorrow I will help my dad clean out our attic.

main idea sentence: _____

_____

detail sentence: _____

_____

detail sentence: _____

_____

detail sentence: _____

_____

Name

Writer's Resources: The Dictionary

A **dictionary** shows how to say and spell words, gives word meanings, and shows how words are used. A dictionary is a long list of words in alphabetical order. When you are looking for a word in a dictionary, follow these steps:

1. Turn to the section of the dictionary that the word is in.

Beginning	**Middle**	**End**
a b c d e f g	h i j k l m n o p q	r s t u v w x y z

2. Find the correct page. Use the pairs of **guide words** at the top of the dictionary page to help you. Guide words tell the first and last words on a page. All words on a page come between the guide words in alphabetical order.

Guide Words ⟶
heater/heel	
heater	Hebrew

A. Circle the section of the dictionary where you would find each word.

1. cheetah   beginning   middle   end

2. earphone   beginning   middle   end

3. saddle   beginning   middle   end

4. turkey   beginning   middle   end

5. plumber   beginning   middle   end

B. Write the correct guide words for each dictionary word. Choose from the guide words in the box.

fly/foil	**fold/foot**	**harm/haste**	**hat/haven**

6. fog   _____   8. harvest   _____

7. have   _____   9. food   _____

Name

Writer's Resources: Dictionary Entries

A **dictionary entry** gives a lot of information about a word.

bow **1.** A weapon for shooting arrows. *He picked up his bow and shot three arrows*. **2.** A slender stick with horsehairs tied along its length. This is pulled across the strings of a violin, cello, etc., to play music. **3.** Anything curved. *A rainbow is a kind of bow*. **4.** A knot tied with loops in it. *The child couldn't tie a bow with his shoestrings*.	← **meaning** ← **sample sentence** ← **another meaning** ← **another meaning** ← **another meaning**

bow (bō) *noun, plural* **bows**

⎿ **number of syllables**

how to say the word
the use of the word

Use the dictionary entry above to answer the following questions.

1. How many meanings are given for *bow*? _____

2. How many sample sentences are given? _____

3. Which meaning has something to do with the sport of archery? _____

4. What would be a good sample sentence for the second meaning?

_____

_____

5. How many syllables are there in the word *bow*? _____

6. Is *bow* a noun or a verb? _____

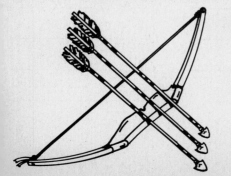

Name

What Is a Noun?

A **noun** is a word that names any person, place or thing.

teacher ⎤ **Person**   street ⎤ **Place**   ball ⎤ **Thing**
student ⎦   playground ⎦   bat ⎦

A. Complete each sentence with the word that makes sense. That word will be a noun.

1. The _____ planned a softball game.   (coach, because, old)

2. The game will be played behind the _____.   (softly, school, into)

3. The _____ will play the girls.   (useful, with, boys)

4. The teams will wear new _____.   (uniforms, keep, today)

5. The winners will get a _____.   (good, visit, trophy)

B. Underline the two nouns in each sentence. Write the nouns on the lines.

6. The sun was in the sky.   _____   _____

7. Parents sat on the ground.   _____   _____

8. The referee tossed a coin.   _____   _____

9. The first girl hit the ball.   _____   _____

10. Three players were on bases.   _____   _____

11. Rain flooded the field.   _____   _____

12. The people ran to their cars.   _____   _____

13. The children got on the bus.   _____   _____

14. The game had no winners.   _____   _____

Singular Nouns and
Plural Nouns

A **singular** noun names only one person, place, or thing.
A **plural** noun names more than one person, place, or thing.
Add **s** to form the plural of most nouns.

| chair | + | s | = | chair<u>s</u> |

Add **es** to form the plural of nouns ending in **s, x, ch,** or **sh.**

| clas<u>s</u> | + | es | = | class<u>es</u> | | di<u>sh</u> | + | es | = | dish<u>es</u> |

Write the correct plural form of each noun in parentheses.

1. Last week the (coachs, coaches) of all the school teams met. _____

2. People from six (schools, schooles) were at the meeting. _____

3. They wanted to discuss how they could interest more (girles, girls) and boys in sports. _____

4. Before the meeting, everyone put their suggestions in (boxes, boxs) by the front door. _____

5. The coaches made a list of their (wishes, wishs) for the coming year. _____

6. When the meeting started, there were several (speechs, speeches). _____

7. Then everyone divided into small (groups, groupes). _____

8. One group talked about the (losses, losss) of the past year. _____

9. Another group talked about things that would make (students, studentes) want to join teams. _____

10. At the end of the meeting, everyone felt that the coming (yeares, years) would be more successful. _____

Name

More Singular Nouns and
Plural Nouns

A **singular** noun names only one person, place, or thing.
A **plural** noun names more than one person, place, or thing.
To form the plural of nouns ending with a vowel and **y,** add **s.**

| turk**ey** | + | s | = | turkey<u>s</u> |

| play | + | s | = | play<u>s</u> |

To form the plural of nouns ending with a consonant and **y,** change
the **y** to **i** and add **es.**

| story | – | y | + | i | + | es | = | stor<u>ies</u> |

| ru**by** | – | y | + | i | + | es | = | rub<u>ies</u> |

A. Underline the correct plural form of each noun.

1. cherrys   cherries
2. tummys   tummies
3. monkeyes   monkeys
4. trays   traies
5. valleys   vallies

6. daisys   daisies
7. jerseys   jerseies
8. buddys   buddies
9. keys   keyes
10. flurry   flurries

B. Underline the correct plural form of each noun in parentheses.

11. For several (days, daies) now, we have been studying a new topic
    in science.
12. We have been studying the (galaxys, galaxies).
13. Many spaceships have made (journeys, journies), but only one has
    left our galaxy.
14. Several (countrys, countries) want to know about outer space.
15. There are many (ways, waies) to study outer space.
16. In some (citys, cities) there are huge telescopes to look at the stars.
17. The (boys, boies) and girls in my neighborhood have formed a
    star club.
18. Sometimes we write (storys, stories) about outer space.
19. We all hope to make great (discoverys, discoveries) in the future.
20. Our (familys, families) hope to look at the stars, too.

Name

More Plural Nouns

> A **singular** noun names only one person, place, or thing.
> A **plural** noun names more than one person, place, or thing.
> Some plural nouns do not follow a regular spelling pattern.
> These nouns have special plural forms.
>
>   man ⟶ men   mouse ⟶ mice
>
> Some nouns have the same singular and plural forms.
>
>   fish ⟶ fish   moose ⟶ moose

A. Underline the correct plural form of each noun.

1. sheep   sheeps
2. gooses   geese
3. children   childs
4. feet   feets
5. oxen   oxes

6. womans   women
7. teeth   tooths
8. deer   deers
9. fishs   fish
10. mans   men

B. On the short blank line, write the plural form of each noun. Then write a sentence that uses each plural noun.

11. mouse   _____

_____

12. sheep   _____

_____

13. woman   _____

_____

14. ox   _____

_____

15. goose   _____

_____

Common Nouns and Proper Nouns

> A **common noun** is a noun that names any person, place or thing.
> A **proper noun** is a noun that names a particular person, place, or thing.
>
> | common nouns | proper nouns |
> |---|---|
> | farmer | Mr. Henry Willis |
> | city | Dallas |
>
> A proper noun begins with a capital letter. In a proper noun of more than one word, each important word begins with a capital letter.

A. Next to each common noun on the left, write the letter of the correct proper noun on the right.

_____ **1.** holiday   a. Thanksgiving
_____ **2.** planet   b. Mississippi River
_____ **3.** state   c. Venus
_____ **4.** month   d. December
_____ **5.** river   e. West Virginia

B. Rewrite each sentence. Replace the underlined words with a proper noun.

6. On our vacation we are going to <u>a foreign country</u>.

_____

7. Can you swim in <u>that lake</u>?

_____

8. Do you know <u>that teacher</u>?

_____

9. I just saw the <u>ocean</u> for the first time.

_____

10. <u>Our doctor</u> met us at the hospital.

_____

Singular Possessive Nouns

> A **possessive noun** ⟶ shows who or what owns or has something.
>
> A singular noun that shows ownership is called a **singular possessive noun.**
>
> Adding **'s** to a singular noun will make it possessive.
>
> | singular noun | + | 's | ⟶ | company | + | 's | = | company's |

A. Write the correct form of each possessive noun in parentheses.

1. This is my _____ favorite radio station.   (sisters's, sister's)

2. The _____ voice is deep.   (announcer's, announcers')

3. I can hardly hear the _____ words.   (singers', singer's)

4. That _____ albums are usually good.

(musician's, musicians's)

5. Soon I will hear the _____ speech.

(president's, presidents')

B. Write the possessive form of each noun in the list.

6. elephant   _____ trunk

7. boy   _____ nose

8. turtle   _____ shell

9. man   _____ skin

10. swan   _____ wings

11. person   _____ arms

12. cat   _____ paws

13. woman   _____ feet

14. bird   _____ feathers

15. girl   _____ hair

Plural Possessive Nouns

> A **possessive noun** ⟶ names who or what owns or has something.
>
> A plural noun that shows ownership is a **plural possessive noun.**
> To make a plural noun show possession, do one of two things.
>
> | plural nouns ending in s | + | ' | ⟶ | dancers | + | ' | = | dancers' |
> | plural nouns not ending in s | + | 's | ⟶ | men | + | 's | = | men's |

A. Write the correct form of each plural possessive noun in parentheses.

1. The _____ pets didn't want to be in the contest.
   (children's, childrens')

2. All the _____ hissing scared the dogs.   (cats's, cats')

3. The _____ barking bothered the other animals.   (dogs', dogs's)

4. The _____ voices announced the winners.   (judges', judges's)

5. The _____ prizes were awarded.   (winners', winners's)

B. Write the correct plural possessive form of each noun in the list.

6. princesses   _____ slippers

7. kings   _____ subjects

8. men   _____ horses

9. horses   _____ hooves

10. knights   _____ armor

11. children   _____ toys

12. villagers   _____ songs

13. women   _____ voices

14. artists   _____ pictures

Name _____

Using Possessive Nouns

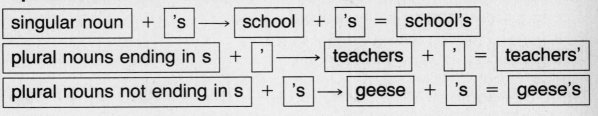

A **possessive noun** names who or what owns or has something.

| singular noun | + | 's | → | school | + | 's | = | school's |

| plural nouns ending in s | + | ' | → | teachers | + | ' | = | teachers' |

| plural nouns not ending in s | + | 's | → | geese | + | 's | = | geese's |

A. Underline the correct possessive form of each noun.

1. monkey   the (monkey's, monkeys') tail
2. children   the (children's, childrens') books
3. doctors   the (doctor's, doctors') patients
4. pilot   the (pilot's, pilots') airplane
5. captain   the (captain's, captains') ship
6. men   the (men's, mens') shirts
7. carpenter   the (carpenter's, carpenters') tools
8. dogs   the (dog's, dogs') ears
9. women   the (women's, womens') jobs
10. athletes   the (athlete's, athletes') sneakers

B. Write the correct possessive form of each noun in parentheses.

11. (farmer)   That _____ fields were just plowed.

12. (workers)   The _____ faces are suntanned.

13. (birds)   Look at the _____ nests in those trees.

14. (children)   I once read a _____ book about a nest.

15. (queen)   The _____ castle sat high on a hill.

Name _____

Mechanics: Abbreviations

An **abbreviation**
  • is a short form of a whole word.
  • usually begins with a capital letter.
  • usually ends with a period.

Titles of People →	Mr.	Mrs.	Ms.	Dr.	Sen.	Gov.	Rep.
Addresses ———→	Ave.	Dr.	St.	Blvd.	Co.	P.O.	Rd.
Days ———————→	Mon.	Tues.	Wed.	Thurs.	Fri.	Sat.	Sun.
Months ————→	Jan.	Feb.	Mar.	Sept.	Oct.	Nov.	Dec.

A. Underline the correct abbreviation for each word.

1. October (Oct., Octob.)
2. Company (Com., Co.)
3. Wednesday (Wed., We.)
4. Boulevard (Blvd., Boulvd.)
5. March (Mar., mar.)
6. Avenue (ave., Ave.)
7. Post Office (Pos. Of., P.O.)
8. Senator (Sen., sen.)
9. Thursday (Th., Thurs.)
10. September (Sep., Sept.)

B. Write the abbreviation for each underlined word.

11. We will be leaving on Sunday. _____

12. Our new home is on Tyler Street in Memphis. _____

13. Doctor Rogers and his family will move into our house. _____

14. Will you come to see me during your vacation in December? _____

15. I will write to you at your home on Daniel Drive. _____

16. Is your birthday in August? _____

17. I will send you a card addressed to Mister Peter Grove. _____

18. Is Governor Land running for office? _____

19. He took a vacation last February. _____

20. Let's get together next Saturday, before I leave. _____

Name _____

Vocabulary Building:
Compound Words

A **compound word** ⟶ is made up of two or more short words joined together.

| row | + | boat | = | rowboat |

| news | + | paper | = | newspaper |

You can often figure out the meaning of a compound word from the meaning of the small words in it.

A. Write the compound word that is made from each pair of words.

1. snow + flake = _____

2. hill + top = _____

3. fire + place = _____

4. loud + speaker = _____

5. suit + case = _____

6. mail + box = _____

7. camp + fire = _____

8. cat + fish = _____

9. play + ground = _____

10. hay + loft = _____

B. Underline the compound word in each sentence.

11. I copied down the homework.
12. After school I put my notebook into my desk.
13. I bought the newspaper on my way home.
14. I ate fresh strawberries for a snack.
15. Finally, I sat down to watch the baseball game.

Name

Grammar and Writing Connection: Combining Sentences

You can sometimes make your writing more clear by combining sentences that have similar ideas. When you combine, use the joining word **and** or **or. And** links ideas. **Or** shows a choice between ideas.

My sister baked muffins.   I baked muffins.

My sister and I baked muffins.

I can make blueberry muffins.   I can make corn muffins.

I can make blueberry or corn muffins.

Combine each pair of sentences using the word in parentheses.

1. I poured the batter into the bowl. I poured milk into the bowl.   (and)

_____

2. My sister will crack the eggs. I will crack the eggs.   (or)

_____

3. We licked the spoon. We licked the bowl.   (and)

_____

4. Dad will turn on the oven. Grandma Grant will turn on the oven.   (or)

_____

5. The muffins smell sweet. The muffins smell delicious.   (and)

_____

6. We will serve some muffins. We will serve some jam.   (and)

_____

7. Dad will set the table. My sister will set the table.   (or)

_____

8. Mom will be surprised. Mom will be happy.   (and)

_____

Name _____

Group Writing:
An Explanation

An **explanation** gives facts and information about a topic. A **topic sentence** states the main idea. **Detail sentences** give facts that support the main idea.

Writing a book report takes time. ←———————— **topic sentence**

First you must find an interesting book. Then you must read the book. Once you complete the book, you can start writing the report. ←— **detail sentences**

A. Read the paragraph. Then follow the directions.

Bowling is one of the oldest sports in the world. It has been played for more than 7,000 years. Balls and pins were found in Egyptian tombs. Bowling, however, goes back even further in history. Pictures found on cave walls show that cavemen played a game like bowling. But, then the balls were rounded rocks, and the pins were pointed stones.

1. Write the topic sentence.

_____

2. Write three detail sentences that support the main idea.

  a. _____

  b. _____

  c. _____

B. Write a detail sentence that could support the main idea expressed in each of the following topic sentences.

3. Topic sentence: Every student should take a music class.

Detail sentence: _____

4. Topic sentence: Living in a warm climate has many advantages.

Detail sentence: _____

Thinking and Writing:
Comparing and Contrasting

> **Comparing** ⟶ details that compare show how things are alike.
> **Contrasting** ⟶ details that contrast show how things are different.
>
> Remember, a paragraph of comparison and contrast should include only those details that will support your topic.
>
> **Comparing:** A bus and a car both have wheels.
> **Contrasting:** A bus is bigger than a car.
> A bus holds more people than a car.

Read the topic for each paragraph. Then write the details that compare in the first column. Write the details that contrast in the second column.

1. Polly is going to write a paragraph about dogs and cats to show which animals make the best pets.

   dogs and cats are friendly   dogs are noisier
   cats can scratch   both animals are fun to have

   Compare   **Contrast**

   a. _____   a. _____

   b. _____   b. _____

2. Turner wants to write a paragraph that compares the Pacific Ocean and the Atlantic Ocean to give information about the two oceans.

   both have salt water   the Pacific Ocean is larger
   the Atlantic Ocean is the most   ships travel on both the Atlantic
     important ocean for trade   and Pacific oceans

   Compare   **Contrast**

   a. _____   a. _____

   b. _____   _____

   _____   b. _____

Name _____

Writer's Resources:
The Library

Fiction	→	books that contain made-up stories *Winnie the Pooh*
Nonfiction	→	books that contain facts and practical information *The Story of Solar Energy*
Reference	→	books of facts and practical information such as dictionaries, encyclopedias, atlases, and directories *Webster's New Collegiate Dictionary*

A. Circle the correct answer.

1. Which of these titles names a fiction book?

The Complete Rhyming Dictionary   *The Secret Garden*

An Introduction to Birds

2. Which of these books would be found on the nonfiction shelves?

Americans in Space   *World Book Encyclopedia*

The Adventures of Pinocchio

3. Which of these titles names a reference book?

Charlotte's Web   *How to Be a Nature Detective*

Century World Atlas

B. In which part of the library would you find each book? Write
fiction, nonfiction, or **reference.**

4. *The Horse in the Attic*   _____

5. *Encyclopedia Britannica*   _____

6. *The Kid in the Red Jacket*   _____

7. *Bridges and How They Are Built*   _____

8. *American Heritage Dictionary*   _____

9. *Sketching Outdoors in Spring*   _____

10. *The Borrowers Aloft*   _____

Writer's Resources:
The Card Catalog

The **card catalog** contains cards on all the books in the library. The cards are filed in alphabetical order. Each book is listed on a title card and on an author card. Every nonfiction book and some fiction books have a subject card, too. Each card has a **call number** in the upper left corner to help find the book.

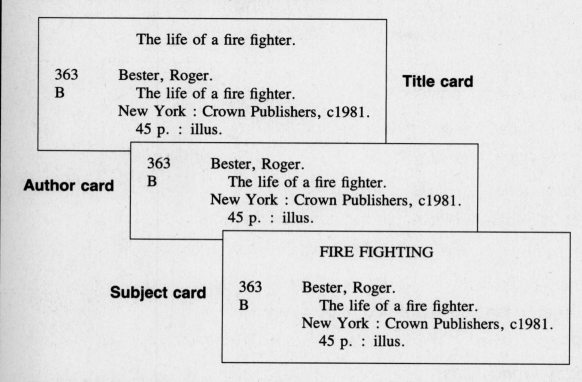

Title card

The life of a fire fighter.

363
B   Bester, Roger.
         The life of a fire fighter.
         New York : Crown Publishers, c1981.
         45 p. : illus.

Author card

363
B   Bester, Roger.
         The life of a fire fighter.
         New York : Crown Publishers, c1981.
         45 p. : illus.

Subject card

FIRE FIGHTING

363
B   Bester, Roger.
         The life of a fire fighter.
         New York : Crown Publishers, c1981.
         45 p. : illus.

A. Use the sample catalog cards above to answer each question.

1. What is the title of the book? _____

2. Who is the author of the book? _____

3. In what year was the book published? _____

B. Underline the card that you would use to find each of the following books.

4. A book by Nancy Johnson   (subject, author, title)

5. A book called *Dogs at Work*   (subject, author, title)

6. A book about the weather   (subject, author, title)

Name

What Is an Action Verb?

An **action verb** $\longrightarrow$ is a verb that expresses action.
tells what the subject does or did.

Brian $\begin{bmatrix} \underline{walks} \\ \underline{skips} \\ \underline{marched} \end{bmatrix}$ to the gym.

A. Underline each action verb.

1. Brian changed his clothes.
2. He put them into a locker.
3. The coach blows his whistle.
4. The boys run onto the basketball court.
5. The coach tosses them a ball.
6. Terry throws the ball to Chris.
7. Chris hurries down the court.
8. He jumped high.
9. Chris scored the first two points.

B. Write the two action verbs in parentheses that make sense in the sentence.

10. The boys (cheer, without, clap) for Chris. _____ _____

11. Daniel (hits, always, taps) the ball. _____ _____

12. Steven (catches, people, grabs) the ball. _____ _____

13. Quickly he (raced, zoomed, into) down the court. _____ _____

14. Steven (pushed, dunked, saw) the ball into the basket! _____ _____

Main Verbs and Helping Verbs

> The **main verb** is the most important verb. A **helping verb** is a verb that comes before the main verb.
>
> **Helping Verbs**
>
> am, is, are, was, were has, have, had, will
>
> **helping main**
>
> A robin   has   built its nest in our tree.

Read each sentence. Write the helping verb in the first column and the main verb in the second column.

1. I am watching the robin. _____ _____

2. It has picked a spot on a big branch. _____ _____

3. The robin's mate is helping with the nest. _____ _____

4. They have found small twigs for the nest. _____ _____

5. The mother bird is putting the twigs in the nest. _____ _____

6. They will use some mud for cement. _____ _____

7. The father bird is carrying a piece of red string. _____ _____

8. The string will make the nest pretty. _____ _____

9. The birds are working hard. _____ _____

10. Yesterday the rain had stopped the birds. _____ _____

Verb Tenses

A **verb** can tell you when an action takes place. The **tense** of a verb tells you if something is happening in the present, in the past, or in the future. A **present tense** verb tells what happens now. A **past tense** verb tells what happened in the past. A **future tense** verb tells what will happen in the future. To write the future tense, use the special verb **will**.

Present Tense	Past Tense	Future Tense
work I <u>work</u> hard now.	worked I <u>worked</u> hard yesterday.	will work I <u>will work</u> hard tomorrow.

A. Write **present tense, past tense,** or **future tense** for each underlined verb.

1. I <u>wake</u> up each morning at six o'clock.   _____

2. The alarm just <u>sits</u> beside my bed.
   I don't need it.   _____

3. Yesterday something terrible <u>happened</u>.   _____

4. My eyes <u>opened</u> at 7:30 A.M.   _____

5. Now I <u>will</u> set my alarm every night.   _____

B. Complete each sentence with a verb from the box that makes sense.

raises	learned	will own	worked	like

6. Last summer I_____ at my grandfather's ranch.

7. My grandfather_____ and sells horses.

8. I_____ his ranch very much.

9. I_____ a lot about horses.

10. One day I_____ a ranch.

Name _____

More About Verb Tenses

> Verbs in the **present tense** tell what happens now.
>   Tom <u>climbs</u> trees.
>
> Verbs in the **past tense** tell what happened in the past.
>   Yesterday Tom <u>climbed</u> a tree.
>
> Verbs in the **future tense** tell what will happen in the future.
> (Use the special verb **will.**)
>   Tomorrow Tom <u>will climb</u> another tree.

A. Circle the correct tense of the underlined verb.

1. Tom <u>runs</u> very fast.   present   past   future
2. He <u>chases</u> rabbits.   present   past   future
3. Yesterday Tom <u>watched</u> a spider.   present   past   future
4. He <u>touched</u> the spider gently.   present   past   future
5. He <u>will celebrate</u> his tenth birthday soon.   present   past   future
6. We <u>will give</u> him a special dinner.   present   past   future
7. He <u>likes</u> tuna very much.   present   past   future
8. Tom <u>gobbled</u> down a whole can yesterday.   present   past   future
9. He <u>will thank</u> us in his own way.   present   past   future
10. By the way, Tom <u>makes</u> a meow sound.   present   past   future

B. Underline the verb that makes sense in each sentence.
Make sure the verb is in the correct tense.

11. Tom is my pet. I (brush, brushed) him every day.
12. His fur (looks, will look) so shiny right now.
13. Yesterday Tom (walks, walked) in some mud.
14. His coat (looks, looked) terrible yesterday.
15. In the future he (stayed, will stay) inside during rainy weather.

Name _____

Subject-Verb Agreement

A verb must **agree** with the subject of a sentence.

singular noun
he, she, or **it** } ⟶ singular verb

Add **s** or **es** to make a verb singular.

Dad <u>swims</u> every morning.

plural noun
I, we, you, or **they** } ⟶ plural verb

To make the verb plural, do **not** add **s** or **es**.

They <u>swim</u> every morning.

A. Write the verb in parentheses that completes each sentence.

1. My parents (work, works) hard on Saturdays. _____

2. Dad (wax, waxes) his car once a month. _____

3. He also (clean, cleans) the attic and garage. _____

4. Mom (visit, visits) my grandparents. _____

5. She (take, takes) homemade muffins to them. _____

B. Write the correct form of the verb in parentheses.

6. Uncle Davis _____ unusual kites.   (make, makes)

7. Children _____ his kites to the park.   (take, takes)

8. Suddenly dragons _____ through the sky.   (soar, soars)

9. Parents _____ them go higher and higher.   (watch, watches)

10. Two kites _____ by the flagpole.   (pass, passes)

Using Irregular Verbs I

You can form the past tense of most verbs by adding the letters **ed** to the verb.

Verbs that do not add **ed** to form the past tense are called **irregular verbs.**

Present	Past	Past with has, have, or had
come	came	has, have, or had come
drive	drove	has, have, or had driven
eat	ate	has, have, or had eaten
give	gave	has, have, or had given
go	went	has, have, or had gone
ride	rode	has, have, or had ridden
run	ran	has, have, or had run
see	saw	has, have, or had seen
write	wrote	has, have, or had written

A. Underline the correct form of the verb in the past tense that completes each sentence.

1. My grandfather (drive, drove) a fire truck for many years.
2. Once I (rode, ride) in the fire truck with him.
3. I (see, saw) all the things inside the truck.
4. I (went, go) with Grandfather during a parade.
5. Many people (came, come) to the parade.

B. Circle the correct form of the verb.

6. I have (gone, went) to the fire station many times.
7. Mom has (came, come) with me a few times.
8. She has (drove, driven) me there in her car.
9. I have (ate, eaten) a few meals at the fire station.
10. I have (seen, saw) the cook in the kitchen.

Name

Using Irregular Verbs II

You can form the past tense of most verbs by adding the letters **ed** to the verb.

Verbs that do not add **ed** to form the past tense are called irregular verbs.

Present	Past	Past with has, have, or had
bring	brought	has, have, or had brought
do	did	has, have, or had done
draw	drew	has, have, or had drawn
fly	flew	has, have, or had flown
grow	grew	has, have, or had grown
make	made	has, have, or had made
sing	sang	has, have, or had sung
swim	swam	has, have, or had swum
take	took	has, have, or had taken
throw	threw	has, have, or had thrown

A. Underline the correct form of the verb in the past tense.

1. Last Saturday my family (did, do) many things.
2. Matt (fly, flew) in a helicopter.
3. Janice (swim, swam) in a swimming meet.
4. My mom (sang, sing) in a concert.
5. Dad (draw, drew) a picture of me.

B. Circle the correct form of the verb in parentheses.

6. My family has (took, taken) several vacations in Florida.

7. We have (bring, brought) our dog Digger with us.

8. Dad has (thrown, threw) a ball into the ocean.

9. Digger has (swim, swum) after it.

10. Digger has (make, made) us all laugh.

Spelling Verbs
Correctly

Some verbs add **s** to form the **present tense.** ——→ wait = waits

Many verbs add **ed** to form the **past tense.** ——→ wait = waited

> **Spelling Rules for Adding es or ed to Some Verbs**
> - Change the **y** to **i** before adding **es** or **ed** to verbs that end with a consonant and **y.** ——→ carry = carries and carried
> - Double the final consonant and add **ed** to verbs that end with one vowel and one consonant. ——→ trim = trimmed
> - Drop the **e** and add **es** or **ed** to verbs that end in **e.** close = closes and closed

A. Underline the correct present-tense or past-tense form of the verb in parentheses.

1. Pete (tryed, tried) to earn some money last week.   past
2. He (carried, carryed) 50 empty bottles back to the store.   past
3. The clerk (grined, grinned) at him.   past
4. "Where were the bottles (stored, storeed)?" the clerk asked.   past
5. "I (dropped, droped) them in bags in the basement," Pete answered.   past
6. The clerk (emptys, empties) a lot of change into Pete's hand.   present
7. He (studies, studys) the change in his hand.   present
8. Then he (charges, chargees) out the door to the nearby video store.   present
9. That afternoon he (invites, invitees) his friends over to see a movie.   present

B. Write the correct past-tense form of the verb in parentheses.

10. I have (flip) through this catalog ten times.   _____

11. I had (worry) about the math test, but I did well.   _____

12. I haven't (notice) the right things yet.   _____

Name

Mechanics:
Using the Comma

When you speak, you pause between words. In writing, **commas** show a reader where to pause. Use commas (,):

- after each word in a **series** except the last word.
  Mercury, Venus, and Earth are the closest planets to the sun.
- to set off a person's name when the person is being directly addressed.
  Terry, did you know that Mercury is the smallest planet?
- after the words **yes, no,** and **well.**
  Yes, the earth is three times bigger than Mercury.

Rewrite each sentence. Use commas where they are needed.

1. There are big rocks craters and mountains on Venus.

_____

2. Yes Venus is the closest planet to Earth.

_____

3. Mrs. Morgan could there be life on Venus?

_____

4. No life cannot exist on Venus.

_____

5. On Mars you would find red dust ice and strong winds.

_____

6. Victor how many moons does Mars have?

_____

7. Well I read that it has two moons.

_____

8. Jupiter has 16 moons a rocky surface and a red spot.

_____

Vocabulary Building:
Prefixes

A **prefix** is a word part added to the beginning of a word. A **base word** is a word to which a prefix is added. A prefix changes the meaning of a base word.

Prefix	Meaning	Example
dis	not, opposite of	dislike (not like)
im	not, without	immovable (not movable)
in	not, without	insecure (not secure)
un	not, opposite of	unwanted (not wanted)
non	not, opposite of, without	nonstop (not stopping)
mis	incorrectly	misplace (place incorrectly)
pre	before	prepaid (paid before)
re	again, back	restate (state again)

To figure out the meaning of a word, put together the meaning of the prefix and the meaning of the base word.

A. Write the letter of the meaning of each word.

_____ **1.** misjudge   **a.** heat again

_____ **2.** pretest   **b.** not fiction

_____ **3.** reheat   **c.** not loyal

_____ **4.** nonfiction   **d.** judge incorrectly

_____ **5.** disloyal   **e.** test before

B. Write a sentence using each word. Use the prefix as a clue to the meaning of the word.

6. unhappy _____

7. impossible _____

8. dishonest _____

9. unable _____

10. imbalance _____

Name _____

Grammar and Writing Connection:
Making Subjects and Verbs Agree

Be sure that subjects and verbs agree in sentences. In sentences with helping verbs, the helping verb in each sentence must also agree with the subject. **Has, have,** and **had** are helping verbs.

Use **has** with a singular subject.

My sister has seen the gymnastic team perform.

Use **have** with plural subjects and **I** and **you**.

The people have seen the gymnastic team perform.
I have seen the gymnastic team perform.

Use **had** with singular or plural subjects.

The man had seen the gymnastic team perform.
The men had seen the gymnastic team perform.

A. Underline the helping verb that correctly completes each sentence.

1. Children of all ages (have, has) come to swimming class.
2. Sara (has, had) started swimming when she was five years old.
3. Her brothers (have, has) always enjoyed swimming.
4. They (has, have) helped her learn how to swim well.
5. In one exercise, you (has, have) to practice kicking in the water.
6. Swimming (have, has) made Sara strong.

B. Write the helping verb **has, have,** or **had** to complete the following sentences.

7. About 500,000 young people across the United
   States ____ practiced gymnastics. _____

8. A gold medal ____ always been a goal in the
   Olympics. _____

9. I ____ wanted to watch gymnastics during the
   Olympics. _____

10. My friends ____ joined a gymnastics club. _____

Group Writing:
A Friendly Letter

A **friendly letter** must have a **purpose** and an **audience.**
The correct form of a **friendly letter** has five parts:

- The **heading** includes your address and the date.
- The **greeting** usually includes the word *dear,* followed by the name of the person to whom you are writing.
- The **body** includes everything that you want to say.
- The **closing** is a way to say "good-bye," such as "Your friend."
- The **signature** is your name, written under the closing.

Think of two events that happened to you last week. Write a letter to a friend or relative and tell that person your news.

_____
_____ } **heading**
_____

_____ , } _____ **greeting**

_____
_____
_____
_____ } **body**
_____
_____
_____

_____ } **closing**

_____ } **signature**

Name

Thinking and Writing:
Solving Problems

To **solve a problem,** it helps to have a plan that includes the following steps:

- State what the problem is.
- State a possible solution.
- List the steps to follow to solve the problem.

Problem	Solution	Steps to Follow
What to do for Mom's birthday	Make her a card.	1. Get paper and crayons. 2. Fold and decorate the paper. 3. Write a note inside.

Underline the solution for each of the following problems. Then circle the steps to follow to reach that solution.

1. **Problem:** How to do well on the baseball team
   Solution: a. Sit in the stands and watch the game.
                     b. Score runs in the next game.

   Steps: Practice hitting.   Watch television.

                   Practice cheering.   Practice running.

2. **Problem:** How to find Jefferson Avenue
   Solution: a. Use a map.
                     b. Take a walk.

   Steps: Have lunch.   Go shopping.

                   Get a map of the area.   Find where you are and where you want to be on the map.

3. **Problem:** What to wear to school
   Solution: a. Check the weather.
                     b. Check the date.

   Steps: Look out the window.   Listen to the radio.

                   Eat breakfast.   Do homework.

Writer's Resources:
Parts of a Book

A book is often divided into parts. Knowing the purpose of each part can help you find information.

Front of a book

- The **title page** is the first page of the book. It tells the title, the author, and the publisher of the book.
- The **copyright page** is after the title page. It tells the date the book was published.
- The **table of contents** lists the chapters and page numbers.

The **body** of a book is the main part of the book. It contains all the parts listed in the table of contents.

Back of a book

- The **glossary** defines special words used in the book.
- The **index** is after the glossary. It lists topics alphabetically and page numbers where the topics can be found in the book.

A. Beside each number, write the letter of the part of the book each student should use to find the information.

_____ **1.** Tony wants to know the name of the person who wrote the book she is reading.

_____ **2.** Erick wants to know which pages in his science book tell about clouds.

_____ **3.** Sue wants to know in what year her reading book was published.

_____ **4.** Carlos wants to know the meaning of the word *tropical.*

a. Title page
b. copyright page
c. index
d. glossary

B. Use your textbook to answer the following questions.

5. On which page does Unit 11 begin? _____

6. Who is the publisher of this book? _____

7. On what page does the *Thesaurus for Writing* begin? _____

What Is a Linking Verb?

An **action verb** tells what the subject does or did.

My cat <u>plays</u> with yarn.

A **linking verb** links the subject of a sentence to a noun or adjective in the predicate. A linking verb does not express action.

My cat <u>is</u> playful.

The words **am, is, are, was,** and **were** are important linking verbs. They are forms of the verb **be.**

My cat <u>is</u> a tabby.   Her stripes <u>are</u> gray.

A. Write whether each underlined verb is an **action verb** or a **linking verb.**

1. My cat's name <u>is</u> Fluffy. _____

2. She <u>purrs</u> a lot. _____

3. Her paws <u>are</u> all white. _____

4. She always <u>cleans</u> her fur. _____

5. Her fur <u>is</u> very soft. _____

B. Underline each verb. Write whether it is an **action verb** or a **linking verb.**

6. Muffin sits by the window every day. _____

7. She watches the people and cars. _____

8. Her favorite food is fish. _____

9. But all of her food disappears quickly. _____

10. I am her cook. _____

11. She gobbles every bit of her food. _____

12. Her plate is very clean. _____

13. Fluffy sleeps on my bed. _____

14. I am a lucky person. _____

Linking Verbs in the Present Tense

Am, is, and **are** are present tense linking verbs. A linking verb must agree with the subject of a sentence. Subjects can be singular or plural.

Subject	Linking Verb

I ⟶ **am**
I am enjoying the book.

she, he, it, or singular noun ⟶ **is**
She is laughing at the funny story.

you, we, they, or plural noun ⟶ **are**
They are reading the same book.

compound subject (two or more things) ⟶ **are**
Both books are well written.

A. Write the correct form of the linking verb in the present tense.

1. This book (is, are) very interesting. _____

2. It (is, are) about music. _____

3. You (is, are) a good piano player. _____

4. I (is, am) a fairly good drummer. _____

5. Beth and Linda (is, are) good singers. _____

6. They (is, are) wonderful when they sing together. _____

B. Draw a line to connect each subject on the left with a predicate on the right. Use the correct linking verb in the present tense.

7. An orchestra   are proud of her.

8. Betsy   am a member of her orchestra.

9. I   is a large group of musicians.

10. Betsy's mom and dad   is an orchestra leader.

Linking Verbs in the Past Tense

Remember that the subject of a sentence can be singular or plural and that a linking verb must agree with the subject of a sentence. **Was** and **were** are past tense linking verbs. Different subjects go with the different verbs.

Subject	**Linking Verb**

I, she, he, it, or singular noun ——————→ **was**
He <u>was</u> at the baseball game yesterday.

you, we, they, or plural noun ——————→ **were**
<u>They were</u> at the baseball game, too.

compound subject (two or more things) ——→ **were**
<u>My friends and my family were</u> both at the same baseball game.

A. Write the correct form of the linking verb in the past tense.

1. I (was, were) in third grade last year.   _____

2. Paul and Elroy (was, were) my best friends.   _____

3. They (was, were) also my next-door neighbors.   _____

4. Mrs. McGregor (was, were) my teacher.   _____

5. She (was, were) very nice.   _____

B. Draw a line to connect each subject on the left with a predicate on the right. Use the correct linking verb in the past tense.

6. Franklin School	was Mr. Valentine.
7. The teachers	were built a few years ago.
8. My principal	were friendly.
9. My mother	was my school last year.
10. A new gym and playground	was once a student at Franklin School.

Using Linking Verbs

When you write, be sure the subject of your sentence agrees with the verb. **Am, is,** and **are** are present tense linking verbs. **Was** and **were** are past tense linking verbs.

Subject	**Linking Verb**
I ————————————————→	**am** and **was**
I am at the library today.	
I was at the library yesterday.	
she, he, it, or singular noun ————→	**is** and **was**
He is at the library now.	
She was at the library before.	
you, we, they, or plural noun ————→	**are** and **were**
Today we are at the library together.	
Last week we were at home.	
compound subject (two or more things) —→	**are** and **were**
The books and magazines are on the shelves.	
The records and films were there last week.	

A. Write the correct linking verb in parentheses.

1. David (is, are) _____ an artist.

2. His pictures (is, are) _____ beautiful.

3. Blue, yellow, and red (was, were) _____ his main colors.

4. He (was, were) _____ delighted with the results.

5. I (is, am) _____ an admirer of fine art.

B. Underline the correct linking verb in parentheses.

6. Mr. and Mrs. Henderson (was, were) our neighbors.
7. They (was, were) very nice.
8. Now the house next door (is, are) empty.
9. We (is, are) sad.

Contractions with *not*

> A **contraction** is a shortened form of two words. An **apostrophe** (')
> takes the place of one or more letters that are left out.
>
> is not ——————→ i s　n o t ——————→ isn ' t ——————→ isn't
>
> is not ——→ isn't　　　　was not ——→ wasn't
> are not ——→ aren't　　　were not ——→ weren't
> has not ——→ hasn't　　　do not ——→ don't
> have not ——→ haven't　　could not ——→ couldn't

A. Write the contraction for each pair of words.

1. should not _____   6. can not _____

2. have not _____   7. is not _____

3. was not _____   8. were not _____

4. did not _____   9. has not _____

5. are not _____   10. would not _____

B. Write the two words that make up each contraction in parentheses.

11. I (don't) _____ remember his name.

12. It (isn't) _____ Thomas.

13. It (couldn't) _____ be Gregory.

14. William and Jeffrey (aren't) _____ even close.

15. I (haven't) _____ the slightest idea what his
name is.

Name

Mechanics: Using Quotation Marks

When you write a speaker's exact words, it is called a **direct quotation.** Use **quotation marks** before and after a direct quotation.

• Use quotation marks to show a speaker's exact words.	"Every beehive has one queen bee," Mrs. Hines said.
• Never use quotation marks around the words that tell who is speaking.	"Some hives have as many as 8,000 bees," she added.
• Do not use quotation marks when you do not use the speaker's exact words.	Nora said that the queen lays all the eggs.

A. Rewrite each sentence. Add quotation marks where they belong.

1. Worker bees also clean the hive, Mrs. Hines added.

_____

2. Soon grubs hatch from the eggs, she said.

_____

3. Nora commented, The grubs are very hungry.

_____

4. The worker bees must feed them, Jeff responded.

_____

B. Read each sentence. Write **correct** next to each sentence that uses quotation marks correctly.

5. "Older worker bees go outside the hive," Mrs. Hines added. _____

6. She told us "that worker bees look for nectar and pollen." _____

7. "Bees make honey from flower nectar," Nora added. _____

8. "Mrs. Hines said," the bees keep the honey in a honeycomb. _____

Vocabulary Building: Suffixes

A **suffix** is a word part that is added to the end of a base word. A suffix changes the meaning of the base word to which it is added.

Suffix	Meaning	Example
able (ible)	capable of, liable to	readable (capable of being read)
er (or)	one who does, that which does	worker (one who works)
ful	full of	powerful (full of power)
less	without	weightless (without weight)
ly	in the manner of	slowly (in a slow manner)
ment	result	retirement (result of being retired)
y	having, being like	rainy (having rain)

A. Write the letter of the meaning that fits each word.

_____ **1.** breakable   **a.** result of being punished

_____ **2.** owner   **b.** one who owns

_____ **3.** guilty   **c.** capable of being broken

_____ **4.** punishment   **d.** having guilt

_____ **5.** lawless   **e.** without any law

_____ **6.** sisterly   **f.** full of hope

_____ **7.** hopeful   **g.** in the manner of a sister

B. Write a sentence for each word. Use the suffix as a clue to the meaning of the word.

8. salty _____

9. fearful _____

10. valueless _____

11. gardener _____

12. normally _____

Grammar and Writing Connection: Combining Sentences

Sometimes sentences have related ideas. When ideas in separate sentences are related, you can join them to make one sentence. Use the word **and** or **but.**

My grandparents | own a ranch.

→ My grandparents | own a ranch and raise horses.

My grandparents | raise horses.

Write each pair of sentences as one sentence by joining the predicates with the word in parentheses.

1. Grandmother meets new workers. She hires them.   (and)

_____

2. Grandfather assigns the chores. He helps the workers.   (and)

_____

3. Each summer I visit them. I can only stay at the ranch for two weeks. (but)

_____

4. I help with the horses. I work for free.   (but)

_____

5. The workers clean out the stalls. They put fresh hay in them.   (and)

_____

6. I ride most of the horses. I avoid Big Red.   (but)

_____

7. Big Red runs very fast. He jumps tall fences.   (and)

_____

8. I work hard at the ranch. I enjoy myself very much.   (but)

_____

Group Writing:
A Story

A story should be entertaining and fun to read. It should have:

- interesting **characters** and **setting.**
  The **characters** are the people in the story. The **main character** is the most important character. The **setting** is where and when the story takes place.

- a good **beginning, middle,** and **end.**
  The **beginning** introduces the characters, the setting, and the **plot,** or the events of the story. In the **middle,** the plot is developed. The main character faces a problem. The **end** tells how the problem is solved.

- a logical **sequence** of events.
  The events in a story often occur in time order.

A. Write whether each item names a **character, setting,** or **problem.**

1. the Kindalls' farm hasn't had rain for two months   _____

2. the next king of England   _____

3. a small island in the Pacific Ocean   _____

4. an Eskimo village in Alaska   _____

B. Think of a story you have read or would like to write. Answer these questions about the story.

5. What is the setting? _____

6. Who is the main character? _____

7. What is the problem that the main character has? _____

_____

8. What is one way the main character might try to solve the problem?

_____

9. How does the story finally end? _____

_____

Thinking and Writing:
Understanding Sequence

> A story's sequence of events should move logically from the beginning through the middle to the end. Events in a story are usually arranged in time order.

Number the events of each plot from 1 to 7 to show the correct sequence, or time order.

1. Setting: Simpson Street Elementary School
Main Character: Bryan O'Leary
Plot:

_____ Bryan calls his mother and asks her to bring him a clean shirt.

_____ Bryan gets the box of paints out of the closet in the art room.

_____ He gets brown paint on his shirt as he is painting a tree.

_____ He takes off his shirt and hangs it up to dry.

_____ He tries to wash off the brown paint, but the spot gets bigger.

_____ Patsy thinks Bryan's shirt is a rag and throws it into the rag pile.

_____ Bryan can't find his shirt.

2. Setting: the imaginary planet Placroton
Main Character: Captain Jake Rawlings
Plot:

_____ Captain Rawlings lands on Placroton.

_____ He digs up the two plants and places them in jars.

_____ Captain Rawlings blasts off from Earth.

_____ While exploring Placroton he discovers two unusual plants.

_____ He avoids being hit by meteorites during the flight to Placroton.

_____ Earth scientists discover that the plants have medicinal qualities.

_____ Captain Rawlings returns to Earth with the plants.

Writer's Resources:
The Thesaurus

A **thesaurus** is a reference book that gives synonyms and antonyms for many words.

Synonyms are words that have the same or almost the same meaning.
Antonyms are words that have an opposite meaning.

The following is a sample entry from a thesaurus.

> **NEW**—*(adj.)* modern, recent, advanced, fresh, unused, unknown,
> beginning, different

The word *new* in the sentence below may be replaced by a synonym for that word from the thesaurus entry.

Amy has a <u>new</u> typewriter.   Amy has a <u>modern</u> typewriter.

A. Use the sample entry to answer the following questions.

1. Would the word *old* be a synonym or an antonym for the word *new?*

_____

2. How many synonyms are given for the word *new?*_____

3. Is *new* used as a noun or an adjective?_____

4. What are two synonyms for *new?*_____

5. Would the words *aged* or *out-of-date* be synonyms or antonyms for the

word *new?*_____

B. For each sentence, circle the synonym that best fits the meaning
of the underlined word.

6. This <u>new</u> head of lettuce is crisp. (recent, unused, fresh)

7. This is a <u>new</u> box of cereal. (modern, unused, beginning)

8. My father works in that <u>new</u> building. (modern, fresh, unknown)

9. That girl is a <u>new</u> student. (advanced, unknown, fresh)

10. I have a <u>new</u> address now. (advanced, beginning, different)

Name _____

What Is an Adjective?

> | are words that describe nouns.
> **Adjectives** ← | can tell **what kind** or **how many.**
> | usually come before the nouns they describe.
>
> red flower   old house   wet shoes
> bright light   cold wind   tall hat

A. Circle the adjective that describes each underlined noun.

1. The animal with the longest <u>nose</u> is the elephant.

2. The elephant is a strong <u>animal</u>.

3. The trunk of the elephant has many <u>uses</u>.

4. With its trunk, an elephant drinks cool <u>water</u>.

5. A dirty <u>elephant</u> cleans itself with water from its trunk.

B. Underline the adjective in each sentence. Write the noun the adjective describes.

6. An elephant can pick up a small berry with its trunk. _____

7. It can also pull up a huge tree out of the ground. _____

8. Elephants do not eat meat; they eat things like green leaves. _____

9. Elephants are smart animals. _____

10. They have been trained to be excellent helpers. _____

11. They can easily move heavy objects. _____

12. Elephants live together in large groups. _____

13. People have killed elephants for their shiny tusks. _____

14. Strict laws now protect elephants. _____

15. Elephants live for many years. _____

Adjectives After Linking Verbs

Sometimes an adjective **follows** the noun it describes. When an adjective follows the noun it describes, the noun and adjective are connected by a linking verb. The linking verb is usually a form of the verb *be*.

Summer is <u>wonderful</u>.   The days are <u>long</u>.

The temperatures are <u>warm</u>.

A. Circle the adjective that describes each underlined noun.

1. <u>Sports</u> in the summer are fun.

2. The pool's <u>water</u> is cool.

3. <u>Food</u> on the grill is delicious.

4. <u>Chicken</u> is tasty when cooked on a grill.

5. In the summer, <u>people</u> are happy.

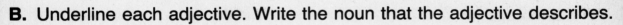

B. Underline each adjective. Write the noun that the adjective describes.

6. That rainbow is beautiful.   _____

7. The colors are bright.   _____

8. The sky is dark.   _____

9. The rain was heavy.   _____

10. The day was dreary.   _____

C. Complete each sentence. Write an adjective that makes sense.

11. I am _____.

12. My home is _____.

13. My family is _____.

14. My friend is _____.

15. School is _____.

Name

Adjectives That Compare

> Adjectives that compare nouns often end in **er** or **est**.
>
> - Adjective + **er** ⟶ compares two nouns.
>
>   A cheetah is <u>faster</u> than a leopard.
>
> - Adjective + **est** ⟶ compares more than two nouns.
>
>   The giraffe is the <u>tallest</u> mammal in the world.

A. Underline the correct form of the adjective in parentheses.

1. The giraffe's neck can be 20 feet long. It has the (longer, longest) neck in the animal kingdom.
2. An ostrich's neck is $4\frac{1}{4}$ feet long. A flamingo's neck is $3\frac{1}{4}$ feet long. The ostrich's neck is (longer, longest) than the flamingo's neck.
3. The cheetah can run at a speed of 71 miles per hour. It is the (faster, fastest) animal in the world.
4. To go one mile, a snail needs 13 days. To go one mile, a tortoise needs about $4\frac{1}{2}$ hours. The snail is (slower, slowest) than the tortoise.
5. An ostrich egg weighs about $3\frac{1}{4}$ pounds. It is the (bigger, biggest) egg in the world.

B. Write the correct form of the adjective in parentheses.

6. This is the (bigger, biggest) book on planets that I have ever seen. _____

7. Did you know that Venus is the (brighter, brightest) planet in the solar system? _____

8. Jupiter is the (bigger, biggest) planet of all. _____

9. Venus is (closer, closest) to the sun than Mars. _____

10. I'm (smarter, smartest) now than I was before I read this book. _____

Name

Spelling Adjectives
That Compare

When adding **er** or **est** to adjectives, follow these spelling rules:

- If an adjective ends with **e,** drop the **e** before adding **er** or **est.**

    little   **littler**   **littlest**

- If an adjective ends with a consonant and **y**, change the **y** to **i** and add **er** or **est.**

    heavy   **heavier**   **heaviest**

- If a one-syllable adjective ends with a consonant-vowel-consonant, double the final consonant before adding **er** or **est.**

    flat   **flatter**   **flattest**

A. Add the endings **er** and **est** to each adjective in the list. Then write the new words on the lines.

	er	est
1. pretty	_____	_____
2. hot	_____	_____
3. wide	_____	_____
4. safe	_____	_____
5. happy	_____	_____

B. Write the correct **er** or **est** form of the adjective in parentheses.

6. (heavy) Which is _____, a ton of rocks or a ton of sand?

7. (silly) That is the _____ joke I have heard all day.

8. (funny) Actually, that is a _____ joke than the one you told me yesterday.

9. (hard) Your jokes are _____ to guess than they were last year.

10. (witty) I think they are the _____ jokes I have ever heard.

Comparing with *more* and *most*

Use **more** and **most** with most adjectives that have two or more syllables.

- To compare two nouns ——————→ **more** + adjective

  This camera is <u>more</u> reliable than that camera.

- To compare more than two nouns ——————→ **most** + adjective

  This camera is the <u>most</u> reliable camera in the store.

Never use **more** or **most** with an adjective that already has an **er** or **est** ending.

This camera is ~~more~~ smaller than that camera.

This camera is the ~~most~~ smallest camera in the store.

A. Write the correct form of the adjective in parentheses.

1. The $140 camera is (more, most) powerful than the $38 camera. _____

2. This camera is (more, most) practical than that one because it fits in your pocket. _____

3. The camera that is on sale takes the (more, most) beautiful pictures of any camera in the store. _____

4. However, the small red camera is the (more, most) popular camera among young people. _____

B. Underline the correct form of the adjective in parentheses.

5. Today is the (most coldest, coldest) day of the year so far.

6. The snow is the (deepest, more deepest) I have ever seen.

7. The skies are (more darker, darker) than they were earlier.

8. I can't wait until it gets (more hotter, hotter) than it is today!

Name

Using Articles

> The words **a, an,** and **the** are special adjectives called **articles.**
>
> • Use **a** before a singular noun that begins with a consonant.
>   <u>a</u> chair   <u>a</u> table
> • Use **an** before a singular noun that begins with a vowel.
>   <u>an</u> arrow   <u>an</u> otter
> • Use **the** before a singular noun that names a particular person, place, or thing.   <u>the</u> deck   <u>the</u> map
> • Use **the** before all plural nouns.   <u>the</u> dogs   <u>the</u> stores

A. Underline each article. Then write the noun that follows each article.

1. Dinosaurs were on the earth about 140 million years ago. _____

2. Stripes on a zebra help it hide from its enemies. _____

3. An anteater actually eats ants. _____

4. Wolves in the United States live in packs. _____

5. A horse can weigh as much as 2,000 pounds. _____

6. At birth a giraffe is $6\frac{1}{2}$ feet tall. _____

7. The ostrich uses its long, powerful toes for defense. _____

8. An elephant often pets her baby with her trunk. _____

B. Complete each sentence with the article **a** or **an.**

9. _____ skunk can squirt out oil from glands near its tail.

10. The spray stings and burns _____ animal's face.

11. It also has _____ taste that is terrible.

12. The spray protects the skunk from _____ enemy.

Name

Mechanics: Capitalizing
Proper Adjectives

A **proper adjective** — [refers to a particular person, place, or thing.

is always capitalized.

Europe ⟶ European ⟶ European cities

North America ⟶ North American ⟶ North American coast

Underline each proper adjective. Then write the noun each proper adjective describes.

1. I have read a lot about American history. _____

2. Leif Ericsson may have been the first European person to come to the Americas. _____

3. Christopher Columbus was an Italian citizen. _____

4. But, he sailed to America for the Spanish queen. _____

5. Columbus actually wanted to get Asian goods. _____

6. Columbus never landed on North American soil. _____

7. A German man who made maps named the Americas after Amerigo Vespucci, an explorer. _____

8. Early Spanish explorers discovered Mexico and other parts of North and Central America. _____

9. Cortés, for example, discovered the city that is now the Mexican capital. _____

10. After coming ashore on the Panamanian coast, Balboa climbed a mountain and discovered the Pacific Ocean. _____

11. Heading south, Pizarro explored the South American continent and found the Inca Indians. _____

12. In 1520, a Portuguese navigator named Magellan landed in what is now Argentina. _____

Name

Vocabulary Building:
Synonyms and Antonyms

Synonyms are words that have the same meaning or almost the same meaning.

tidy/neat   fast/quick   small/tiny

Antonyms are words that have opposite meanings.

tidy/messy   fast/slow   kind/unkind

Some antonyms can be formed by adding the prefix **un.**

able = unable   happy = unhappy

A. Circle the word in parentheses that is a **synonym** for the underlined word.

1. When I am in a play, I get nervous. (calm, jumpy, nice)

2. My stomach feels funny, and my heart starts to beat fast. (stop, pound, hit)

3. My mind goes blank, and I can't remember my lines. (dizzy, empty, full)

4. But when the curtain goes up, I feel fearless. (brave, cowardly, faint)

5. Plays I have been in have all been successful. (short, worthless, rewarding)

B. Circle the word in parentheses that is an **antonym** for the underlined word.

6. Last Saturday I went upstairs into our dreary attic. (dark, dull, bright)

7. I first spotted a sturdy old trunk. (strong, strange, weak)

8. When I opened it, I smelled an unpleasant odor. (pleasant, terrible, unlikeable)

9. It was only the musty smell of old books. (ancient, new, used)

10. Inside the trunk was a beautiful picture of my mother as a young girl. (handsome, ugly, boring)

Name

Grammar and Writing Connection:
Choosing Vivid Adjectives

A **vivid adjective** is one that makes your word picture very clear.

That restaurant has <u>good</u> food.

That restaurant has <u>tasty</u> food. ← more precise

A. Write the adjective in parentheses that is more exact.

1. Last night we ate at a restaurant with a (spectacular, nice) _____ view.

2. We could see a (pretty, blazing) _____ sunset.

3. We were seated at a (clean, spotless) _____ table.

4. A (charming, nice) _____ waiter gave us menus.

5. I ordered some (good, spicy) _____ Italian food.

6. We all enjoyed our (delicious, nice) _____ dinners.

7. Then the waiter brought us (huge, big) _____ desserts.

8. The (sweet, good) _____ desserts quickly vanished.

9. The restaurant played (soft, pleasant) _____ dinner music.

10. Everyone had a (fine, wonderful) _____ time.

B. Write a colorful, vivid adjective on each blank line.

11. The _____ fair was an _____ event.

12. _____ musicians played their instruments before _____ crowds.

13. The _____ aroma of food drifted through the tents.

14. _____ owners led their animals before the judges.

15. By eight o'clock, _____ people headed toward their homes.

Group Writing:
A Description

> The **purpose** of a description is to create a clear and vivid picture. The following help make a picture clear and vivid for the audience:
> - An Overall Impression ⟶ the general idea
> - Sensory Details ⟶ tell more about how things look, sound, taste, feel, or smell
> - Logical Order ⟶ details arranged in an order that is logical

A. Read the sentence and think about what the writer was trying to describe. Then write a sensory detail sentence that uses each of the following words.

As we hiked slowly through the woods, we were awed by nature's many beautiful masterpieces.

silky _____

spicy _____

prickly _____

rushing _____

B. Arrange the details below in a logical order.

_____ Then she looked out the window and saw snow.

_____ Her mother had breakfast waiting for her.

_____ Finally, Sue got her books and went to school.

_____ First, Sue turned the alarm clock off and got out of bed.

_____ After she got dressed, Sue went to the kitchen.

_____ When she finished breakfast, Sue got her coat.

_____ Then she put on her boots.

_____ Sue knew she had better put on some warm clothes.

Name

Thinking and Writing:
Classifying Sensory Details

When you write a **description** you will have to decide which details
are important. Include **details** that tell more about the overall
impression.

My father painted my room. ⟶ overall impression

It is a light blue color.
The walls are wet.   ⟶ important details
The paint smells strong.

I went to play baseball.   details that do not add
We ate chicken for dinner.   ⟶ to the overall impression

A. Read each idea for a description. Then underline the details that
should be included.

1. Raymond is going to write a description of the greenhouse his father
owns. He wants to create an overall impression of the greenhouse as a
wonderful place to work.

lovely flowers growing everywhere   very hot and humid
hands always in dirt and fertilizer   lots of cheerful sunlight

2. Susanne wants to write a description of the kitchen in her house. She
wants to create an overall impression of the kitchen as a warm, cozy
place to be on a winter's afternoon.

dirty dishes stacked in the sink   sunlight pouring through the window
noisy, as people come and go   smell of muffins baking

B. Write another detail that could be included in both Raymond's and
Susanne's descriptions.

3. Raymond's description: _____

4. Susanne's description: _____

Writer's Resources:
The Encyclopedia

An **encyclopedia** is a set of books that contains information about many subjects. Encyclopedia articles give information about people, places, things and events.

- Each book, or volume, in the set has articles that are arranged in alphabetical order.

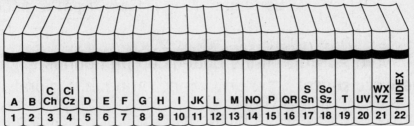

- The volumes are labeled with one or more letters. Each volume includes subjects beginning with that letter.

Every encyclopedia has an **index** that lists all the subjects written about in the encyclopedia.

A. Circle the number of the encyclopedia volume that would contain information on each of the following subjects. Use the set of encyclopedias above.

1. Connecticut

   3   4   19

3. hockey

   9   11   15

5. Ohio

   9   11   14

2. Eagles

   1   6   17

4. Lake Michigan

   12   13   17

6. peanuts

   2   15   20

B. Match each animal name with the volume that would have an article on the subject. Draw a line between the name and the box that stands for the volume.

7. caribou

8. camel

9. chimpanzee

| C–Ch |

| Ci–Cz |

10. cougar

11. coyote

12. cheetah

Name

What Is a Pronoun?

A **pronoun** is a word that takes the place of one or more nouns.

Singular Pronouns:	I, you, he, she, it, me, him, her
Plural Pronouns:	we, you, they, us, them

noun: The dogs are barking.   Give the dogs a biscuit.
pronoun: They are barking.   Give them a biscuit.

A. Circle the word **singular** if the underlined pronoun is singular. Circle the word **plural** if the underlined pronoun is plural.

1. I saw Leroy painting some pictures.   singular   plural
2. He gave them to his mother.   singular   plural
3. Mrs. Franklin, the art teacher, saw them.   singular   plural
4. She said that Leroy will be a great artist one day.   singular   plural
5. Leroy went with them to the art show.   singular   plural

B. Underline the pronoun in parentheses that correctly completes the second sentence. Use the underlined word or words as clues.

6. Last week Leroy painted a picture of his dog.
   (He, They) has painted many pictures of animals.

7. Greg and I watched Leroy paint one day.
   (Us, We) were very interested.

8. Greg asked Leroy for one of the pictures.
   Leroy gave (him, it) a picture of a lion.

9. Greg showed the picture to his parents.
   (We, They) liked it very much.

10. His parents even bought a frame for the picture.
    Greg hung (it, them) in his room.

Name _____

Subject Pronouns

> A **subject pronoun** is a pronoun that is used as the subject of a sentence.
>
> ### Subject Pronouns
>
> | | |
> |---|---|
> | **Singular:** | I, you, he, she, it |
> | **Plural:** | we, you, they |
>
> Patty is here.   Chris and Don came late.
> She is here.   They came late.

A. Underline the subject pronoun in each sentence.

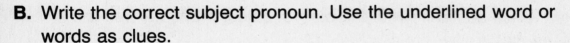

1. Wanda is my sister. She is 15 years old.
2. I like to take hikes.
3. We often hike together.
4. You should come along some day.
5. Hiking is good exercise. It is fun, too.

B. Write the correct subject pronoun. Use the underlined word or words as clues.

6. Last Saturday Dad wanted to go on a picnic. _____ quickly packed the picnic basket.

7. Mom and I liked the idea. _____ got out a map.

8. Mom found several interesting parks. _____ finally chose one about 15 miles away.

9. At the park, forest rangers were riding on horses. _____ were there to help people.

10. Mom, Dad, and I had a wonderful time that day. _____ plan to have another picnic very soon.

Name

Object Pronouns

An **object pronoun** is a pronoun that is used in the predicate of a sentence. It may follow an action verb or a word such as **in, into, to, with, for, by,** or **at.**

Object Pronouns

Singular:	**me, you, him, her, it**
Plural:	**us, you, them**

The children ate the <u>raisins</u>. The children ate <u>them</u>.

A. Underline the object pronoun in each sentence.

1. I like reading very much. Sometimes Mrs. Smith tells me to read aloud.
2. I think Bryan is the best reader. Mrs. Smith asks him to read often.
3. Mrs. Smith helps us with hard words.
4. Sometimes she describes different books. Then she gives them out.
5. Mrs. Smith is a wonderful teacher. The class likes her very much.

B. Complete each sentence with the correct object pronoun. Use the underlined word or words as clues.

6. Summer vacation begins soon for <u>Wade and me</u>. Our grandparents have

   invited _____ to their home in Arizona.

7. <u>Grandfather Frey</u> flies a small airplane.

   We always ask _____ for a ride.

8. I will have a birthday in Arizona. My grandparents might give

   _____ a party.

9. We always have a wonderful time with <u>our grandparents</u>. We will send

   _____ a thank-you letter.

Name _____

Possessive Pronouns

A **possessive pronoun** shows who or what owns something. A possessive pronoun takes the place of one or more possessive nouns.

Possessive Pronouns

Singular:	**my, your, his, her, its**
Plural:	**our, your, their**

Cindy took swimming lessons.

Her teacher was very good.

Mother and Father drove Cindy to the pool.

Their car is getting old.

A. Underline the possessive pronoun in each sentence.

1. I took swimming lessons last summer. My lessons lasted for six weeks.
2. Miss Davis was the teacher. Her first name was Susie.
3. There were six other children in the class. Their parents watched the lessons.
4. Lance Hodges was in the class. His father is the police chief.
5. Have you ever taken swimming lessons? Your swimming would improve with lessons.

B. Write the correct possessive pronoun. Use the underlined word or words as clues.

6. Once I tried to swim in the ocean. That was the summer

   _____ family went to Cape Cod.

7. First my brother Jack jumped into the water. He yelled when the cold

   water hit _____ body.

8. Jack and I hated the ocean's salty taste. _____ parents

   didn't seem to mind it.

9. Mom and Dad floated on top of the water. _____ bodies

   bobbed up and down.

Using *I* and *me* Correctly

I ──→ Use in the subject of a sentence.

I collect stamps.   ~~Me~~ collect stamps.

me ──→Use after an action verb or words such as **in, into, with, by,** or **at.**

Dad tells me about stamps.   Dad tells ~~I~~ about stamps.

A. Underline the correct word in parentheses.

1. (I, me) have collected many interesting stamps.
2. Dad helps (I, me) with the stamps.
3. He always gives (I, me) good advice.
4. What he knows about stamps always surprises (I, me).
5. Tomorrow (I, me) will buy four new stamps.

B. Write the word **I** or **me** to complete each sentence.

6. _____ joined a stamp club.

7. My friend Eric invited _____ to a meeting.

8. Stamps interest _____ a lot.

9. _____ took my stamp books to the meeting.

10. Eric introduced _____ to everyone.

11. _____ traded stamps with one member.

12. _____ gave her a one-cent stamp.

13. She gave _____ a two-cent stamp.

14. _____ had a wonderful time at the meeting.

15. Eric will call _____ for the next meeting.

Name _____

Mechanics: Pronoun Contractions

> A **contraction** is a word made up of two words.
>
> | | | | |
> |---|---|---|---|
> | I am | → I'm | we are | → we're |
> | they will | → they'll | you have | → you've |
> | she is | → she's | he had | → he'd |
> | she has | → she's | he would | → he'd |
>
> An **apostrophe (')** shows that one or more letters are missing.
>
> I will → I ⬚wi⬚ ll → I ⬚'⬚ ll → I'll

A. Underline each contraction. Then write the two words that make up the contraction.

1. I'm glad it is a sunny day. _____

2. We're wasting time. _____

3. She's got a good idea. _____

4. They'll like it a lot. _____

5. You've never played basketball in the park? _____

6. I'll be a forward. _____

7. He'd be a good guard. _____

8. They'll have enough players for a second team. _____

9. He'd rather be on that team. _____

10. We're having a great time! _____

B. Underline each pair of words that could be a contraction. Then write the contraction.

11. She has left her lunch under her desk. _____

12. I will take it to her. _____

13. She will be thankful. _____

14. You are a thoughtful person. _____

15. I am glad I could help. _____

Vocabulary Building:
Homophones and Homographs

Homophones are words that sound the same but have different spellings and meanings.

weak—not strong	**week**—seven days
I'm too <u>weak</u> to lift that box.	I'll call you in a <u>week</u>.

Homographs are words that are spelled the same but have different meanings. Some homographs also have different pronunciations.

lead (pronounced lĕd) a metal	**lead** (pronounced lēd) to guide
This <u>lead</u> pipe weighs a lot.	Will you <u>lead</u> us to the stables?

A. Underline the correct word in parentheses.

1. A (knew, new) student just came to our school.
2. (Their, There) are some things she didn't know about the school.
3. For example, one day she broke the (heel, heal) of her shoe.
4. One (piece, peace) of her shoe was on her foot and the other was in her hand.
5. She asked (to, two) classmates what to do.
6. They (cent, sent) her to the art room.
7. If you (brake, break) anything, the art room is the place to go.
8. (It's, Its) on the main floor.
9. The girl didn't (waste, waist) any time.
10. Her shoe (seems, seams) to be all right now.

B. Write the word from the box that correctly completes the sentence.

post	present	palm

11. In what states do _____ trees grow?

12. We should _____ this picture on the bulletin board.

13. I had to return one _____ I got for my birthday.

14. The boy placed the coins in the _____ of his hand.

15. Who will _____ the awards for the best costume?

Name

Grammar and Writing Connection:
Combining Sentences

When you combine two or more sentences, you may list several words in a row. This list is called a **series.**

- Place the word **and** or **or** before the last word in a series.
- Words in a series are separated by commas.

Sometimes you can combine sentences by adding words in a series.

| Markers | were in the art room.

| Paints | were in the art room. | Markers, | paints, | and | brushes |

| Brushes | were in the art room.   were in the art room.

Combine these groups of sentences by joining words in a series.

1. Mrs. Miller helped Tod.
Mrs. Miller helped David.
Mrs. Miller helped Louis.

_____

2. Did David use red?
Did David use blue?
Did David use white?

_____

3. Horses were in Tod's picture.
Cows were in Tod's picture.
Pigs were in Tod's picture.

_____

4. Old photographs were on Louis's poster.
Magazine pictures were on Louis's poster.
Drawings were on Louis's poster.

_____

Name _____

Group Writing: A Persuasive Paragraph

The **purpose** of a persuasive paragraph is to **convince an audience** to feel the way the writer does.

- Opinions stated clearly ⟶ The topic sentence usually states the opinion.

- Order of reasons ⟶ Reasons that support the opinion follow, with the most important reasons given first.

- Facts that support the opinions ⟶ Back up the opinion with facts. Facts help persuade the audience that the opinion is sound.

A. State your opinion about each of the following topics. Write your opinion in the form of a topic sentence for a persuasive paragraph.

1. television _____

2. movies _____

B. Read the following persuasive paragraph. Then answer the questions.

Bicycle riders should have to wear helmets. Helmets would prevent minor head injuries. They would also prevent more serious head injuries, which are sometimes fatal. The number of injured motorcycle riders fell sharply when they had to wear helmets. If bicycle riders had to wear helmets, the number of injured bicycle riders would also fall.

3. What is the writer's opinion? _____

4. What is the first reason given to support that opinion? _____

_____

5. What is a fact given to support the opinion? _____

_____

6. Did this persuasive paragraph make you agree with the writer? Explain why or why not. _____

Name

Thinking and Writing:
Telling Fact from Opinion

A **fact** is a statement that can be proved or checked.
An **opinion** is something that is believed. It cannot be proved or checked.

A. Write **fact** if the statement is a fact or **opinion** if the statement is an opinion.

1. I think that everyone should get involved in a sport. _____

2. Baseball is a sport in which you play on a team. _____

3. In tennis, there are either two or four players. _____

4. Football is more fun to play than soccer. _____

5. In a basketball game, points are scored when the ball goes into the net. _____

6. People who play ice hockey must know how to skate. _____

7. You will enjoy sports more if you have a favorite team that you can watch play. _____

B. What is your opinion about sports? Do you have a favorite sport or a favorite team? Why do you like this particular sport or team?

8. Write your opinion about sports. Write it in the form of a topic sentence for a persuasive paragraph.

_____

_____

9. Write one fact to support your topic sentence. _____

_____

10. Write one opinion to support your topic sentence. _____

_____

Name

Writer's Resources: The Atlas and the Almanac

An **atlas** is a book of maps. It usually contains several kinds of maps for one area.

An **almanac** gives facts about populations, current events, famous people, sports, elections, and many other subjects. A new almanac is published every year. It provides up-to-date information.

Circle **atlas** or **almanac** to tell where you would find the answer to each question.

1. What United States city has the largest population?   almanac   atlas

2. Where is the capital of Spain located?   almanac   atlas

3. On which of the Hawaiian Islands is Honolulu located?   almanac   atlas

4. What are the abbreviations for all the states?   almanac   atlas

5. Who is the president of Ireland?   almanac   atlas

6. What should you do if someone is choking?   almanac   atlas

7. Is Greece closer to Turkey or to Switzerland?   almanac   atlas

8. In what ocean is the island of Madagascar?   almanac   atlas

9. What state is directly north of Nebraska?   almanac   atlas

10. In what state is Bennett College located?   almanac   atlas

11. What was the population of the United States in 1610?   almanac   atlas

12. Who won the Grammy Awards last year?   almanac   atlas

13. What is Pearl Buck known for?   almanac   atlas

14. What is the largest lake in Nevada?   almanac   atlas

15. What is the closest Canadian province to Prince Edward Island?   almanac   atlas

What Is an Adverb?

An **adverb** is a word that tells more about a verb.

An adverb tells **when** an action takes place.

    how
    where

I <u>happily</u> go to camp. ——→ tells <u>how</u>
I <u>never</u> miss camp. ——→ tells <u>when</u>
My cabin is <u>there</u>. ——→ tells <u>where</u>

Many adverbs end with **ly.**

A. Underline each adverb.

1. Come inside with me.
2. My bunk is here.
3. Sometimes I listen to the crickets.
4. Crickets live everywhere.
5. The crickets call loudly to one another.

B. Underline each adverb. Then write the verb that each adverb describes.

6. Soon I fall asleep.   _____

7. Then the bugle plays.   _____

8. It easily wakes us.   _____

9. I always make my bed.   _____

10. We rush outside for roll call.   _____

11. Suddenly rain begins.   _____

12. Rain rarely falls.   _____

13. The counselors quickly cancel all outdoor _____
  activities.

14. We eat breakfast slowly.   _____

15. That day lasted forever.   _____

Name _____

More About Adverbs

An **adverb** is a word that tells more about a verb. It tells **how, when,** or **where.** An adverb can be put at the beginning of a sentence, before or after the verb, or at the end of a sentence. If you use an adverb to begin a sentence, place a comma after it.

<u>Slowly</u>, Tom walked to school.
Tom walked <u>slowly</u> to school.
Tom <u>slowly</u> walked to school.
Tom walked to school <u>slowly</u>.

A. Circle the question that each underlined adverb answers.

1. I <u>really</u> enjoy puzzles.	where	when	how
2. <u>There</u> is the hardest puzzle!	where	when	how
3. I work on the puzzles <u>regularly</u>.	where	when	how
4. I <u>often</u> do a puzzle instead of watching TV.	where	when	how
5. I work <u>here</u>.	where	when	how
6. This lamp shines <u>brightly</u>.	where	when	how
7. <u>Sometimes</u>, my father helps me.	where	when	how
8. He works <u>carefully</u>.	where	when	how
9. I have completed another puzzle <u>successfully</u>.	where	when	how
10. Each piece fits <u>perfectly</u>.	where	when	how

B. Write the correct word in parentheses.

11. I (easy, easily) find the border pieces. _____

12. (Slow, Slowly), the puzzle takes shape. _____

13. The face of the dog can be seen (clearly, clear). _____

14. (Quick, Quickly), I find the missing pieces. _____

15. I (happy, happily) place the last piece. _____

Name

Using Adverbs to Compare

An **adverb** can be used to make comparisons.
Short adverbs:

- Add **er** to compare two actions.
  This horse jumped <u>higher</u> than that horse.
- Add **est** to compare more than two actions.
  Of all the horses in the contest, this one jumped the <u>highest</u>.

The words **more** and **most** are usually used to form comparisons with adverbs that end in **ly** and with longer adverbs.

- Use **more** to compare two actions.
  This horse ran <u>more quickly</u> than that horse.
- Use **most** to compare more than two actions.
  Of all the horses in the contest, this one ran the <u>most quickly</u>.

Underline the word or words in parentheses that correctly complete each sentence.

1. Of all local events, our county fair is the (more enjoyable, most enjoyable).
2. I arrived at the fair (earlier, earliest) than my friend Jeb.
3. Last year Mr. Jenson's pig ate (more quickly, most quickly) than Jeb's pig.
4. Of all the other children, I usually cut the wool off my sheep the (more neatly, most neatly).
5. The person who cuts the wool off the (more quickly, most quickly) is the winner.
6. Last year I cut (faster, fastest) than Jeb.
7. In one contest, the pet frog that reaches the finish line the (sooner, soonest) wins a prize.
8. Of all the frogs in that contest, my frog jumped the (more swiftly, most swiftly).
9. My dad's workhorse won a prize by pulling the (harder, hardest) of all the horses.

Name _____

Using *good* and *well*
Correctly

> **Good** is an adjective. It describes a noun.
>
> > It may come before a noun. → That was <u>good</u> food.
> > It may follow a linking verb. → That food was <u>good</u>.
>
> **Well** is usually an adverb. It tells more about a verb.
>
> > My mother cooks <u>well</u>.

A. Underline the correct word in parentheses.

1. This science-fiction book is (good, well).
2. Stories about the future are always (good, well).
3. Of course, the action has to be written (good, well).
4. Then I can imagine the story (good, well).
5. To me, (good, well) books are better than movies.

B. Write **good** or **well** to complete each sentence.

6. These are _____ sneakers.

7. They help me run _____ .

8. There is _____ padding in the bottom.

9. The softness is _____ for my feet.

10. The sneakers wear _____ .

11. The laces work _____ .

12. White is a _____ color for sneakers.

13. These sneakers are _____ for both walking and running.

14. Exercise is important for _____ health.

15. With these sneakers I should do _____ in all sports.

Name

Negatives

Some sentences include the word **no,** or other words that mean "no." These words are called **negatives.** Some negatives contain *no.*

Negatives ——→

no	none	no one	nowhere
not	never	nobody	nothing
Others include the contraction **n't.**			

Never use two negatives in a sentence. ——→ I didn't see ~~no one~~.
Change one of the negatives without
changing the meaning of the sentence. ——→ I didn't see anyone.

I saw no one.

A. Underline the word that correctly completes each sentence.

1. I won't (never, ever) go to a scary movie again.
2. I couldn't look at (none, any) of the monsters.
3. There wasn't (anywhere, nowhere) for me to go except the lobby.
4. I didn't like (any, none) of the special effects.
5. I can't find (one, no) good thing to say about scary movies.

B. Rewrite each incorrect sentence. Substitute a positive word for one negative word.

6. Isn't no one going to help me with this puzzle?

_____

7. I can't even find nobody to collect all the pieces.

_____

8. There's a corner piece that I can't find nowhere.

_____

9. I shouldn't have never started this puzzle.

_____

10. This isn't no way to have fun.

_____

Mechanics: Punctuating Titles

When you write, you may need to name a book or story that you have read. When you write titles, there are certain rules to follow.

- The first, last, and all important words in a title should be capitalized.

  <u>The Wonderful Wizard of Oz</u>

- Underline titles of books, magazines, and newspapers.

  Books ⟶ <u>The Case of the Missing Clock</u>
  Newspapers ⟶ <u>Chicago Tribune</u>
  Magazines ⟶ <u>Reader's Digest</u>

- Use quotation marks to punctuate titles of articles, stories, songs, and poems.

  Article ⟶ "Watching Whales"
  Story ⟶ "Killer Whale"
  Song ⟶ "Three Jolly Fishermen"
  Poem ⟶ "Where Go the Boats"

Circle the title in parentheses that is written correctly.

1. I have just finished reading the book (<u>Myths and Folklore</u>, Myths and Folklore).

2. I have a subscription to the magazine (<u>Young Athlete</u>, Young Athlete).

3. The local newspaper, the (Warren Newsbeat, <u>Warren Newsbeat</u>), prints the scores of the Little League games.

4. (<u>Animal Atlas of the world</u>, <u>Animal Atlas of the World</u>) is a very interesting book.

5. Mom just read an article called ("Fun Things for Rainy Days", Fun Things for Rainy Days).

6. The (<u>New York Times</u>, <u>new york times</u>) is one of the biggest newspapers in the United States.

7. She read the story (Frog in The Pond, "Frog in the Pond").

Vocabulary Building:
Borrowed Words

The English language has many words that come from other languages.

Borrowed words — are words that come from other languages.

are words that became part of our own language with time.

(Spanish) guitarra ⟶ (English) guitar

A dictionary often will tell you from which language a borrowed word comes.

Use each borrowed word in a sentence. If a word is unfamiliar, look up its meaning in a dictionary.

1. (American Indian) pecan _____

_____

2. (Spanish) tornado _____

_____

3. (French) prairie _____

_____

4. (Portuguese) zebra _____

_____

5. (German) frankfurter _____

_____

6. (Italian) macaroni _____

_____

7. (Latin) video _____

_____

Name

Grammar and Writing Connection:
Combining Sentences

When you use words and phrases in your own writing that tell **how, where,** or **when,** look for ways to combine sentences that have similar ideas.

Our dog Morgan chases rabbits <u>often</u>. ——→ tells **when**
Our dog Morgan chases rabbits <u>eagerly</u>. ——→ tells **how**
Our dog Morgan chases rabbits <u>outside</u>. ——→ tells **where**
Our dog Morgan often chases rabbits eagerly in the backyard.

Write a word or phrase that answers the question in parentheses. Then combine the groups of sentences by joining words that tell **how, where,** or **when.**

1. Morgan sees a rabbit.

   He sees a rabbit (where?) _____ .

   _____

2. Morgan's tail points.

   It points (where?) _____ .

   _____

3. He chases the rabbit.

   He chases it (how?) _____ .

   _____

4. Morgan catches a rabbit.

   (when?) _____ he catches one.

   _____

5. (How?) _____ Morgan carries the rabbit.

   He carries it (where?) _____ .

   _____

Group Writing:
A Research Report

The **purpose** of a research report is to give information to an **audience** about a specific topic.

- **Notetaking** ⟶ Taking notes will help you to remember what you have read. Write only main ideas and important details.
- **Outlining** ⟶ An **outline** helps you to organize a report. Use your notes to list items in the order in which you wish to discuss them.

Title

I. Main topic ⟶ will be a paragraph
   A. Detail that supports the main topic ⟶ subtopic
   B. Detail that supports the main topic ⟶ subtopic

- **Organizing Information Logically** ⟶ A research report should be organized in a logical manner so that the reader can easily follow the ideas that you wish to present.

Here is the first part of an outline. Read it and answer the questions.

Superman

I. Powers of Superman
   A. Can fly very fast
   B. X-ray vision
   C. Super strength
   D. Super hearing

1. What is the main topic of this outline? _____

2. How many details support the main idea? _____

3. What is the last detail presented? _____

4. What would the notes for this outline be about? _____

5. If you were writing a report based on this part of the outline, how many paragraphs would you write? Explain your answer. _____

_____

Thinking and Writing:
Summarizing

A **summary** tells the most important ideas of a longer piece of writing. A summary is short. It gives only the main idea and facts that the audience will need to know.

When you summarize information, — keep your audience and purpose in mind.

choose only those details that are the most important.

Write a three-sentence summary of this report for members of your science club.

Animals' Tails

Tails are not just a nice addition that animals have and people don't. Tails have different purposes for different animals, but all of the purposes are important. For example, animals may use their tails to communicate, for warmth, for balance, for hanging, and for grabbing things.

When a dog sleeps, it curls its tail around itself to keep warm. However, when it wakes up, it will wag its tail to tell you it's happy. White-tailed deer also communicate with their tails. If there's danger, they raise their tails straight up like flags.

A kangaroo's tail is very important. Without it, a kangaroo couldn't keep its balance. Squirrels and monkeys also use their tails for balance. Cows, on the other hand, use their tails to push away pesty flies.

_____

_____

_____

_____

Name _____

Writer's Resources: Graphs, Tables, and Maps

Writers consult special resources to locate facts. Some possible resources are graphs, tables, and maps.
Graphs and **tables** are good ways of showing information about numbers.

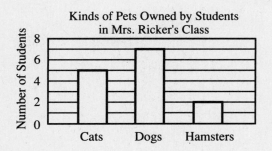

Kinds of Pets Owned by Students in Mrs. Ricker's Class

Kinds of Pets Owned by Students at Emerson Elementary School

PETS	BOYS	GIRLS	TOTAL
Dogs	56	33	89
Cats	64	81	145
Hamsters	8	2	10

Maps also give facts. They show where things are and how far one place is from another.

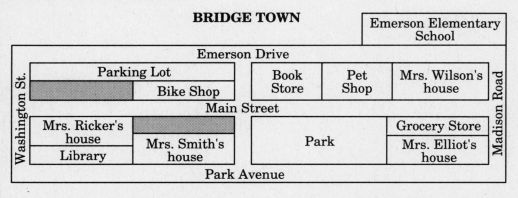

Use the graph, table, or map to answer the following questions.

1. How many students own dogs in Mrs. Ricker's class? _____

2. Which pet do the fewest number of students in Mrs. Ricker's class have?

_____

3. What is the most popular pet at Emerson Elementary School? _____

4. How many boys own dogs at Emerson Elementary School? _____

5. When you leave the pet shop, do you go north or south to the school?

_____

Name _____

What Is a Sentence?

A **sentence** is a group of words that expresses a complete thought.

> ASK Does the group of words express a complete thought?
> Does it tell about a person or thing and what the person or thing did?

If the answer to both questions is yes, then the group of words is a sentence. If the answer is *no*, then the group of words is not a sentence.

Patsy's cat ran up a tree. = a sentence
Up a tree. = not a sentence

A. Underline each sentence.

1. One day Patsy couldn't find her cat.

2. Called and called her cat.

3. Patsy called and called for him.

4. She looked under the porch.
   Under the porch.

5. Soon the sky would get dark.
   Soon the sky.

6. Sometimes the cat.
   Sometimes the cat goes to the park.

7. Patsy walked through the park.
   Through the park.

8. A small meow.
   She heard a small meow.

9. The sound came from a tree.
   Came from a tree.

10. Her cat was on the top branch.
    On the top branch.

B. Write whether each group of words is or is not a **sentence**.

11. Ran to a telephone. _____ not a sentence

12. Patsy called the fire department. _____ sentence

13. The fire truck raced down the street. _____ sentence

14. Noise of the fire truck. _____ not a sentence

15. The cat ran down the tree. _____ sentence

Name _____

Declarative and Interrogative Sentences

A declarative sentence makes a statement. ——→ Insects have six legs.
An interrogative sentence asks a question. ——→ Do insects have six legs?

A. Underline each sentence that tells something.

1. Insects have three parts to their bodies.

2. They also have feelers and wings.

3. Are spiders insects?

4. Spiders have eight legs and no wings.

5. Do spiders have two or three parts to their bodies?

B. Underline each sentence that asks something.

6. A fly is an insect.

7. Can flies walk upside down?

8. Do flies smell with their feelers?

9. How fast do the wings of a fly move?

10. A fly's wings beat about 200 times a minute.

C. Follow the directions. (Answers will vary.)

11. Write a sentence that tells something about an insect. Put a period at the end of your sentence.

    A bee is an insect.
    _____

12. Write a sentence that asks something about an insect. Put a question mark at the end of your sentence.

    Does a bee sting hurt?
    _____

T1

Imperative and Exclamatory Sentences

An **imperative sentence** can tell or ask someone to do something. ——→ Cut the meat.

An **exclamatory sentence** can show strong feeling. ——→ What lean meat this is!

A. Underline each sentence that tells or asks someone to do something.

1. Wash the vegetables carefully.
2. How hot the water is!
3. Peel the potatoes.
4. Throw the skins in the garbage can.
5. That garbage can smells bad!

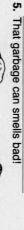
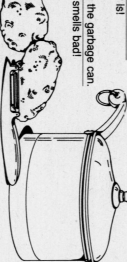

B. Underline each sentence that shows strong feeling.

6. Quick, the water is boiling over!
7. Turn the heat down.
8. Put the potatoes into the water.
9. Cook the potatoes for about 20 minutes.
10. What a delicious stew you made!

C. Follow the directions. (Answers will vary.)

11. Write a sentence that tells or asks someone to do something about cooking. Put a period at the end of your sentence.

    Chop the carrots and onions.

12. Write a sentence that shows strong feeling about cooking. Put an exclamation point at the end of your sentence.

    Your stew is burning!

Complete Subjects and Complete Predicates

A **complete subject**, or subject part, ——→ includes all the words that tell whom or what the sentence is about.

A **complete predicate**, or predicate part, ——→ includes all the words that tell what the subject does or is.

Read this sentence.

My family ——→ goes to the park.

complete subject   complete predicate

A. Finish each sentence with a complete subject from the box.

All ants	Some children	A few dogs
Colorful flowers		Two squirrels

1. Two squirrels _____ look for nuts to eat.
2. All ants _____ have two antennae.
3. Some children _____ ride bicycles.
4. Colorful flowers _____ bloom in a garden.
5. A few dogs _____ bark loudly.

B. Finish each sentence with a complete predicate from the box.

blows through the trees	flies his kite	rocks her baby
swim in the pond	eats a big worm	

6. Some fish _swim in the pond_ _____.
7. A little boy _flies his kite_ _____.
8. A mother _rocks her baby_ _____.
9. A robin _eats a big worm_ _____.
10. A warm breeze _blows through the trees_ _____.

Simple Subjects

The **complete subject** includes all the words that tell whom or what the sentence is about.

> My mother ⌐ gave my sister a birthday party.

The **simple subject** is the main word or group of words in the complete subject.

A. Underline the complete subject. Then write the simple subject.

1. Many children came to the party. _____ children
2. Colorful balloons were everywhere. _____ balloons
3. Many presents sat beside a chair. _____ presents
4. One large box was covered with blue paper. _____ box
5. My sister opened the presents. _____ sister

B. Circle the simple subject.

6. Our next-door (neighbor) gave her a book.
7. A silly (clown) jumped out of one box.
8. The (children) laughed with surprise.
9. Our grey (cat) played in the wrapping paper.
10. My (parents) took pictures at the party.

C. Complete each sentence with a simple subject that makes sense.
(Answers will vary.)

11. My _____ grandmother made the food for the party.
12. The _____ sandwiches tasted delicious.
13. The _____ people at the party ate all the food.
14. Our little _____ dog gobbled up the crumbs on the floor.
15. All the _____ guests left the party at five o'clock.

Simple Predicates

The **complete predicate** includes all the words that tell what the subject does or is.

> My class ⌐ took a trip to a fire station.

The **simple predicate** is the main word or group of words in the complete predicate.

A. Underline the complete predicate. Then write the simple predicate.

1. The chief meets us at the door. _____ meets
2. The children walk inside the station. _____ walk
3. Some fire fighters eat their breakfasts. _____ eat
4. Other fire fighters polish a fire engine. _____ polish
5. The children talk to the fire fighters. _____ talk

B. Circle each simple predicate.

6. A young dog (runs) around the station.
7. The fire fighters (named) him Rex.
8. Rex (barks) loudly sometimes.
9. The children (love) Rex.
10. The black and white dog (lives) at the fire station.

C. Complete each sentence with a simple predicate that makes sense. (Answers will vary.)

11. The alarm _____ rings very loudly.
12. The fire fighters _____ run to the fire engine.
13. The doors of the fire station _____ open quickly.
14. The fire engines _____ race down the street.
15. The children _____ watch the fire engines.

Name _____

Compound Subjects and Compound Predicates

A **compound subject** is two or more simple subjects that have the same predicate. The simple subjects are joined by **and.**

The girls ─┐
            ├ and ├─ put on a variety show.
the boys ──┘

A **compound predicate** is two or more simple predicates that have the same subject. The simple predicates are joined by **and.**

Katie ─┐ plays the piano
        ├ and ├
        └ sings a song.

A. Underline the compound subject in each sentence.

1. Linda and Kelly sing a duet.
2. My sister and brother perform bicycle tricks.
3. My good friend and her neighbor dance with taps on their shoes.
4. My teacher and her husband play trumpets.
5. My family and friends sit in the audience.

B. Underline the compound predicate in each sentence.

6. Mr. Davis fixes and works the lights.
7. Dad rents and borrows some chairs.
8. Other helpers cook and serve refreshments.
9. The performers smile and bow at the end of the show.
10. The audience claps and cheers.

Name _____

Correcting Run-on Sentences

A **run-on sentence** contains two or more sentences that run together. To fix a run-on sentence, break it into shorter sentences.

People grow grapes and the sun dries the grapes.

People grow grapes.   The sun dries the grapes.
                    and

they become raisins.

They become raisins.

Fix each run-on sentence by breaking it into shorter sentences. Write the new sentences on the lines.

1. Many people grow grapes and some growers live in California and some live in other warm places in the world.

   Many people grow grapes. Some growers live in California. Some live in other warm places in the world.

2. A farmer raises grapes in a vineyard and the grapes hang on a vine and they grow in bunches.

   A farmer raises grapes in a vineyard. The grapes hang on a vine. They grow in bunches.

3. Then workers pick the grapes and they put the grapes on wooden trays and the sun shines on the grapes for many days.

   Then workers pick the grapes. They put the grapes on wooden trays. The sun shines on the grapes for many days.

4. The grapes become wrinkled and their green color turns to a blackish brown and finally they are raisins.

   The grapes become wrinkled. Their green color turns to a blackish brown. Finally they are raisins.

T4

Mechanics: Punctuating Sentences

RETEACHING·9

Every sentence must begin with a capital letter.

A **declarative** sentence makes a statement or tells something.
It ends with a period. ⟶ A boat ride is fun.

An **imperative** sentence tells or asks someone to do something.
It ends with a period. ⟶ Don't drop the oars.

An **interrogative** sentence asks something.
It ends with a question mark. ⟶ Do you like boat rides?

An **exclamatory** sentence shows strong feeling.
It ends with an exclamation point. ⟶ Boat rides are exciting!

Write each sentence correctly. Add a capital letter and the correct end punctuation.

1. this boat is a canoe
   This boat is a canoe. _____

2. don't rock the canoe
   Don't rock the canoe. _____

3. why must we be so careful
   Why must we be so careful? _____

4. a canoe can tip over easily
   A canoe can tip over easily. _____

5. should I paddle like this
   Should I paddle like this? _____

6. stop, we're heading for those rocks
   Stop, we're heading for those rocks! _____

Vocabulary Building: Using Context Clues

RETEACHING·10

Context clues are the words that come before and after an unfamiliar word in a sentence.

The context clues in the following sentence can help you understand the meaning of the word *descends*.

A waterfall is a stream that *descends* suddenly from a higher level to a lower level.

The words *from a higher level to a lower level* tell you that *descends* means "goes down."

Read each sentence and look for context clues. Then write the correct meaning of each underlined word.

1. The water in some waterfalls <u>plunges</u> hundreds of feet to the bottom.
   falls quickly   flows upward   falls quickly _____

2. Other waterfalls are not very high, but their <u>breadth</u> is great.
   height   width   width _____

3. If the <u>volume</u> of water in a waterfall is small, there is not enough water to produce electricity.
   temperature   amount   amount _____

4. The <u>immense</u> size of some waterfalls creates breathtaking scenery.
   large   small   large _____

5. Angels Falls, the world's highest falls, crash straight down, <u>uninterrupted</u> by rocks.
   stopped briefly   without being stopped   without being stopped _____

6. In 1935, James Angel was the first American to <u>espy</u> the Angels Falls with his own eyes.
   see   name   see _____

T5

Grammar and Writing Connection: Combining Sentences

Use the words **and** or **but** to connect two sentences. **And** means "in addition."

| All birds have wings. | + | Most birds can fly. |

All birds have wings, **and** most birds can fly.

But shows a contrast.

| Ostriches cannot fly. | + | They can run very fast. |

Ostriches cannot fly, **but** they can run very fast.

Remember to put a comma before the joining word.

Combine each pair of sentences. Use the word in parentheses to join the sentences.

1. Some birds fly at night. Others fly during the day.   (but)

   Some birds fly at night, but others fly during the day.

2. The hummingbird is the smallest bird. The ostrich is the largest bird.   (and)

   The hummingbird is the smallest bird, and the ostrich is the largest bird.

3. Birds sit on their eggs. The heat makes the chicks grow.   (and)

   Birds sit on their eggs, and the heat makes the chicks grow.

4. Some small birds live on seeds. Hawks eat rabbits and snakes.   (but)

   Some small birds live on seeds, but hawks eat rabbits and snakes.

Group Writing: A Personal Narrative

- A **personal narrative** tells something about what has happened to the writer.
- A personal narrative should have an **interesting beginning sentence** which tells the **main idea.**
- A personal narrative also contains **detail sentences** which support, or say more about, the main idea.
- A personal narrative should be written in time order, the events are told in the order in which they actually happened.

Time order   First event ——→ I jumped into the pool.
       Second event ——→ I swam for an hour.
       Third event ——→ I dried off in the sun.

Read the following personal narratives. Then list the details from each narrative in the correct time order.

1. I was so excited about using my new roller skates, that I could hardly wait to bring them home! The first thing I did was to strap them on my feet. Then I skated down the sidewalk. I was skating well, until I suddenly lost my balance and fell.

First event: I strapped my skates on my feet.

Second event: I skated down the sidewalk.

Third event: I lost my balance and fell.

2. I wanted to send my grandmother something special. First, I got some paper, scissors, and colored pencils. Then, I spent the afternoon making her a beautiful card. Finally, I wrote her a letter inside the card.

First event: I got some paper, scissors, and colored pencils.

Second event: I made a beautiful card.

Third event: I wrote a letter inside the card.

Name

Thinking and Writing:
Main Idea and Details

- A personal narrative has a **main idea**. It can be the beginning sentence. It tells what the narrative will be about.
- The other sentences in the narrative are **detail sentences**. They support the main idea, or tell more information about it.

main idea sentence → I'll never forget the time I marched in a Memorial Day Parade.

detail sentences → I wore my cub scout uniform.
I carried a flag.
I had sore feet the next day.

Read the paragraph. On the lines below, write the main idea sentence and the three detail sentences that support it. Put a line through the sentence in the paragraph that does not support the main idea.

Helping My Neighbor

Because my neighbor is recovering from an illness, I help her with her chores. Every Friday I shop for her at the grocery store. Sometimes I go to the post office for her. Yesterday, I raked the leaves in her yard. Tomorrow I will help my dad clean out our attic.

main idea sentence:

Because my neighbor is recovering from an illness, I help her with her chores.

detail sentence:

Every Friday I shop for her at the grocery store.

detail sentence:

Sometimes I go to the post office for her.

detail sentence:

Yesterday, I raked the leaves in her yard.

Name

Writer's Resources:
The Dictionary

A **dictionary** shows how to say and spell words, gives word meanings, and shows how words are used. A dictionary is a long list of words in alphabetical order. When you are looking for a word in a dictionary, follow these steps:

1. Turn to the section of the dictionary that the word is in.

Beginning	Middle	End
a b c d e f g	h i j k l m n o p q	r s t u v w x y z

2. Find the correct page. Use the pairs of **guide words** at the top of the dictionary page to help you. Guide words tell the first and last words on a page. All words on a page come between the guide words in alphabetical order.

Guide Words →
heater/heel
heater
Hebrew

A. Circle the section of the dictionary where you would find each word.

1. cheetah — beginning — (middle) — end
2. earphone — (beginning) — middle — end
3. saddle — beginning — middle — (end)
4. turkey — beginning — middle — (end)
5. plumber — beginning — (middle) — end

B. Write the correct guide words for each dictionary word. Choose from the guide words in the box.

fly/foil	fold/foot	harm/haste	hat/haven

6. fog — fly/foil
7. have — hat/haven
8. harvest — harm/haste
9. food — fold/foot

Writer's Resources:
Dictionary Entries

A **dictionary entry** gives a lot of information about a word.

> bow **1.** A weapon for shooting arrows. *He picked up his bow and shot three arrows.* **2.** A slender stick with horsehairs tied along its length. This is pulled across the strings of a violin, cello, etc., to play music.
> **3.** Anything curved. *A rainbow is a kind of bow.* **4.** A knot tied with loops in it. *The child couldn't tie a bow with his shoestrings.*
>
> **bow** (bō) *noun, plural* **bows**

— meaning
— sample sentence
— another meaning

— another meaning
— another meaning

— number of syllables

— how to say the word
— the use of the word

Use the dictionary entry above to answer the following questions.

1. How many meanings are given for *bow*? __4__

2. How many sample sentences are given? __3__

3. Which meaning has something to do with the sport of archery? __1__

4. What would be a good sample sentence for the second meaning? (Answers will vary.) **The musician slowly drew his bow over the strings of his violin.**

5. How many syllables are there in the word *bow*? __one__

6. Is *bow* a noun or a verb? __a noun__

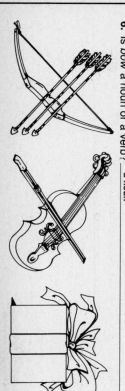

What Is a Noun?

A **noun** is a word that names any person, place or thing.

Person	Place	Thing
teacher	street	ball
student	playground	bat

A. Complete each sentence with the word that makes sense. That word will be a noun.

1. The _____ **coach** _____ planned a softball game. (coach, because, old)

2. The game will be played behind the _____ **school** _____. (softly, school, into)

3. The _____ **boys** _____ will play the girls. (useful, with, boys)

4. The teams will wear new _____ **uniforms** _____. (uniforms, keep, today)

5. The winners will get a _____ **trophy** _____. (good, visit, trophy)

B. Underline the two nouns in each sentence. Write the nouns on the lines.

6. The <u>sun</u> was in the <u>sky</u>. — sun — sky

7. <u>Parents</u> sat on the <u>ground</u>. — parents — ground

8. The <u>referee</u> tossed a <u>coin</u>. — referee — coin

9. The first <u>girl</u> hit the <u>ball</u>. — girl — ball

10. Three <u>players</u> were on <u>bases</u>. — players — bases

11. <u>Rain</u> flooded the <u>field</u>. — rain — field

12. The <u>people</u> ran to their <u>cars</u>. — people — cars

13. The <u>children</u> got on the <u>bus</u>. — children — bus

14. The <u>game</u> had no <u>winners</u>. — game — winners

Name _____

Singular Nouns and Plural Nouns

A **singular** noun names only one person, place, or thing.
A **plural** noun names more than one person, place, or thing.
Add **s** to form the plural of most nouns.

chair + s = chairs

Add **es** to form the plural of nouns ending in **s, x, ch,** or **sh.**

class + es = classes
dish + es = dishes

Write the correct plural form of each noun in parentheses.

1. Last week the (coachs, coaches) of all the school teams met. _____ coaches

2. People from six (schools, schooles) were at the meeting. _____ schools

3. They wanted to discuss how they could interest more (girles, girls) and boys in sports. _____ girls

4. Before the meeting, everyone put their suggestions in (boxes, boxs) by the front door. _____ boxes

5. The coaches made a list of their (wishes, wishs) for the coming year. _____ wishes

6. When the meeting started, there were several (speechs, speeches). _____ speeches

7. Then everyone divided into small (groups, groupes). _____ groups

8. One group talked about the (losses, losss) of the past year. _____ losses

9. Another group talked about things that would make (students, studentes) want to join teams. _____ students

10. At the end of the meeting, everyone felt that the coming (yeares, years) would be more successful. _____ years

Macmillan LANGUAGE ARTS TODAY
Grade 4, Unit 3, Lesson 2, pages 78–79

Name _____

More Singular Nouns and Plural Nouns

A **singular** noun names only one person, place, or thing.
A **plural** noun names more than one person, place, or thing.
To form the plural of nouns ending with a vowel and **y,** add **s.**

turkey + s = turkeys
play + s = plays

To form the plural of nouns ending with a consonant and **y,** change the **y** to **i** and add **es.**

story – y + i + es = stories
ruby – y + i + es = rubies

A. Underline the correct plural form of each noun.

1. cherrys / cherries
2. tummys / tummies
3. monkeyes / monkeys
4. trays / traies
5. valleys / vallies
6. daisys / daisies
7. jerseys / jerseies
8. buddys / buddies
9. keys / keyes
10. flurry / flurries

B. Underline the correct plural form of each noun in parentheses.

11. For several (days, daies) now, we have been studying a new topic in science.
12. We have been studying the (galaxys, galaxies).
13. Many spaceships have made (journeys, journies), but only one has left our galaxy.
14. Several (countrys, countries) want to know about outer space.
15. There are many (ways, waies) to study outer space.
16. In some (citys, cities) there are huge telescopes to look at the stars.
17. The (boys, boies) and girls in my neighborhood have formed a star club.
18. Sometimes we write (storys, stories) about outer space.
19. We all hope to make great (discoverys, discoveries) in the future.
20. Our (familys, families) hope to look at the stars, too.

Macmillan LANGUAGE ARTS TODAY
Grade 4, Unit 3, Lesson 3, pages 80–81

More Plural Nouns

A **singular** noun names only one person, place, or thing.
A **plural** noun names more than one person, place, or thing.
Some plural nouns do not follow a regular spelling pattern.
These nouns have special plural forms.

man → men	mouse → mice	

Some nouns have the same singular and plural forms.

fish → fish	moose → moose	

A. Underline the correct plural form of each noun.

1. sheep	sheeps	<u>sheep</u>	**6.** womans	<u>women</u>	
2. gooses	<u>geese</u>	geese	**7.** <u>teeth</u>	tooths	
3. children	childs		**8.** <u>deer</u>	deers	
4. <u>feet</u>	feets		**9.** <u>fish</u>	fish	
5. <u>oxen</u>	oxes		**10.** mans	<u>men</u>	

B. On the short blank line, write the plural form of each noun. Then write a sentence that uses each plural noun. (Sentences will vary.)

11. mouse _____ mice _____
Sometimes my cat catches mice.

12. sheep _____ sheep _____
How many sheep are in that field?

13. woman _____ women _____
There are five women in my family.

14. ox _____ oxen _____
The oxen slowly pulled the cart up the hill.

15. goose _____ geese _____
Many geese land here every fall on their way south.

Common Nouns and Proper Nouns

A **common noun** is a noun that names any person, place or thing.
A **proper noun** is a noun that names a particular person, place, or thing.

common nouns	proper nouns
farmer	Mr. Henry Willis
city	Dallas

A proper noun begins with a capital letter. In a proper noun of more than one word, each important word begins with a capital letter.

A. Next to each common noun on the left, write the letter of the correct proper noun on the right.

a	**1.** holiday	a.	Thanksgiving
c	**2.** planet	b.	Mississippi River
e	**3.** state	c.	Venus
d	**4.** month	d.	December
b	**5.** river	e.	West Virginia

B. Rewrite each sentence. Replace the underlined words with a proper noun. (Answers will vary.)

6. On our vacation we are going to a <u>foreign country</u>.
On our vacation we are going to England.

7. Can you swim in <u>that lake</u>?
Can you swim in Lake Michigan?

8. Do you know <u>that teacher</u>?
Do you know Mr. Johnson?

9. I just saw the <u>ocean</u> for the first time.
I just saw the Atlantic Ocean for the first time.

10. Our <u>doctor</u> met us at the hospital.
Dr. Anderson met us at the hospital.

Singular Possessive Nouns

RETEACHING-21

A **possessive noun** → shows who or what owns or has something.

A singular noun that shows ownership is called a **singular possessive noun**.

Adding **'s** to a singular noun will make it possessive.

singular noun	+	's	→	company	+	's	=	company's

A. Write the correct form of each possessive noun in parentheses.

1. This is my ___ sister's ___ favorite radio station. (sisters's, sister's)

2. The ___ announcer's ___ voice is deep. (announcer's, announcers')

3. I can hardly hear the ___ singer's ___ words. (singers', singer's)

4. That ___ musician's ___ albums are usually good. (musician's, musicians's)

5. Soon I will hear the ___ president's ___ speech. (president's, presidents')

B. Write the possessive form of each noun in the list.

6. elephant ___ elephant's ___ trunk

7. boy ___ boy's ___ nose

8. turtle ___ turtle's ___ shell

9. man ___ man's ___ skin

10. swan ___ swan's ___ wings

11. person ___ person's ___ arms

12. cat ___ cat's ___ paws

13. woman ___ woman's ___ feet

14. bird ___ bird's ___ feathers

15. girl ___ girl's ___ hair

Plural Possessive Nouns

RETEACHING-22

A **possessive noun** → names who or what owns or has something.

A plural noun that shows ownership is a **plural possessive noun**.

To make a plural noun show possession, do one of two things.

plural nouns ending in s	+	'	→	dancers	+	'	=	dancers'
plural nouns not ending in s	+	's	→	men	+	's	=	men's

A. Write the correct form of each plural possessive noun in parentheses.

1. The ___ children's ___ pets didn't want to be in the contest. (children's, childrens')

2. All the ___ cats' ___ hissing scared the dogs. (cats's, cats')

3. The ___ dogs' ___ barking bothered the other animals. (dogs', dogs's)

4. The ___ judges' ___ voices announced the winners. (judges', judges's)

5. The ___ winners' ___ prizes were awarded. (winners', winners's)

B. Write the correct plural possessive form of each noun in the list.

6. princesses ___ princesses' ___ slippers

7. kings ___ kings' ___ subjects

8. men ___ men's ___ horses

9. horses ___ horses' ___ hooves

10. knights ___ knights' ___ armor

11. children ___ children's ___ toys

12. villagers ___ villagers' ___ songs

13. women ___ women's ___ voices

14. artists ___ artists' ___ pictures

T11

Using Possessive Nouns

A **possessive noun** names who or what owns or has something.

singular noun	+	's	→	school	+	's	=	school's
plural nouns ending in s	+	'		teachers	+	's	=	teachers'
plural nouns not ending in s	+	's		geese	+	's	=	geese's

A. Underline the correct possessive form of each noun.

1. monkey — the (monkey's, monkeys') tail
2. children — the (children's, childrens') books
3. doctors — the (doctor's, doctors') patients
4. pilot — the (pilot's, pilots') airplane
5. captain — the (captain's, captains') ship
6. men — the (men's, mens') shirts
7. carpenter — the (carpenter's, carpenters') tools
8. dogs — the (dog's, dogs') ears
9. women — the (women's, womens') jobs
10. athletes — the (athlete's, athletes') sneakers

B. Write the correct possessive form of each noun in parentheses.

11. (farmer) That _____ farmer's _____ fields were just plowed.
12. (workers) The _____ workers' _____ faces are suntanned.
13. (birds) Look at the _____ birds' _____ nests in those trees.
14. (children) I once read a _____ children's _____ book about a nest.
15. (queen) The _____ queen's _____ castle sat high on a hill.

Mechanics: Abbreviations

An **abbreviation**
- is a short form of a whole word.
- usually begins with a capital letter.
- usually ends with a period.

Titles of People →	Mr.	Mrs.	Ms.	Dr.	Sen.	Gov.	Rep.
Addresses →	Ave.	Dr.	St.	Blvd.	Co.	P.O.	Rd.
Days →	Mon.	Tues.	Wed.	Thurs.	Fri.	Sat.	Sun.
Months →	Jan.	Feb.	Mar.	Sept.	Oct.	Nov.	Dec.

A. Underline the correct abbreviation for each word.

1. October (Oct., Octob.)
2. Company (Com., Co.)
3. Wednesday (Wed., We.)
4. Boulevard (Blvd., Boulvd.)
5. March (Mar., mar.)
6. Avenue (ave., Ave.)
7. Post Office (Pos. Of., P.O.)
8. Senator (Sen., sen.)
9. Thursday (Th., Thurs.)
10. September (Sep., Sept.)

B. Write the abbreviation for each underlined word.

11. We will be leaving on <u>Sunday</u>. _____ Sun.
12. Our new home is on Tyler <u>Street</u> in Memphis. _____ St.
13. <u>Doctor</u> Rogers and his family will move into our house. _____ Dr.
14. Will you come to see me during your vacation in <u>December</u>? _____ Dec.
15. I will write to you at your home on Daniel <u>Drive</u>. _____ Dr.
16. Is your birthday in <u>August</u>? _____ Aug.
17. I will send you a card addressed to <u>Mister</u> Peter Grove. _____ Mr.
18. Is <u>Governor</u> Land running for office? _____ Gov.
19. He took a vacation last <u>February</u>. _____ Feb.
20. Let's get together next <u>Saturday</u>, before I leave. _____ Sat.

Vocabulary Building: Compound Words

A **compound word** → is made up of two or more short words joined together.

| row | + | boat | = | rowboat |

| news | + | paper | = | newspaper |

You can often figure out the meaning of a compound word from the meaning of the small words in it.

A. Write the compound word that is made from each pair of words.

1. snow + flake = **snowflake**
2. hill + top = **hilltop**
3. fire + place = **fireplace**
4. loud + speaker = **loudspeaker**
5. suit + case = **suitcase**
6. mail + box = **mailbox**
7. camp + fire = **campfire**
8. cat + fish = **catfish**
9. play + ground = **playground**
10. hay + loft = **hayloft**

B. Underline the compound word in each sentence.

11. I copied down the homework.
12. After school I put my notebook into my desk.
13. I bought the newspaper on my way home.
14. I ate fresh strawberries for a snack.
15. Finally, I sat down to watch the baseball game.

Grammar and Writing Connection: Combining Sentences

You can sometimes make your writing more clear by combining sentences that have similar ideas. When you combine, use the joining word **and** or **or**. **And** links ideas. **Or** shows a choice between ideas.

| My sister | baked muffins. |

| My sister and I baked muffins. |

| I | baked muffins. |

| I can make | blueberry muffins. |

| I can make blueberry or corn muffins. |

| I can make | corn muffins. |

Combine each pair of sentences using the word in parentheses.

1. I poured the batter into the bowl. I poured milk into the bowl. (and)
   I poured the batter and the milk into the bowl.

2. My sister will crack the eggs. I will crack the eggs. (or)
   My sister or I will crack the eggs.

3. We licked the spoon. We licked the bowl. (and)
   We licked the spoon and the bowl.

4. Dad will turn on the oven. Grandma Grant will turn on the oven. (or)
   Dad or Grandma Grant will turn on the oven.

5. The muffins smell sweet. The muffins smell delicious. (and)
   The muffins smell sweet and delicious.

6. We will serve some muffins. We will serve some jam. (and)
   We will serve some muffins and jam.

7. Dad will set the table. My sister will set the table. (or)
   Dad or my sister will set the table.

8. Mom will be surprised. Mom will be happy. (and)
   Mom will be surprised and happy.

T13

Name

Group Writing:
An Explanation

An **explanation** gives facts and information about a topic. A **topic sentence** states the main idea. **Detail sentences** give facts that support the main idea.

Writing a book report takes time. ⟶ topic sentence

First you must find an interesting book. Then you must read the book. Once you complete the book, you can start writing the report. ⟶ detail sentences

A. Read the paragraph. Then follow the directions.

Bowling is one of the oldest sports in the world. It has been played for more than 7,000 years. Balls and pins were found in Egyptian tombs. Bowling, however, goes back even further in history. Pictures found on cave walls show that cavemen played a game like bowling. But, then the balls were rounded rocks, and the pins were pointed stones.

1. Write the topic sentence.

   Bowling is one of the oldest sports in the world.

2. Write three detail sentences that support the main idea.

   a. It has been played for more than 7,000 years.

   b. Balls and pins have been found in Egyptian tombs.

   c. Pictures found on cave walls show that cavemen played a game like bowling.

B. Write a detail sentence that could support the main idea expressed in each of the following topic sentences. (Answers will vary.)

3. Topic sentence: Every student should take a music class.

   Detail sentence: The class will help students understand the music they hear.

4. Topic sentence: Living in a warm climate has many advantages.

   Detail sentence: People do not have to drive in the snow.

Name

Thinking and Writing:
Comparing and Contrasting

Comparing ⟶ details that compare show how things are alike.
Contrasting ⟶ details that contrast show how things are different.

Remember, a paragraph of comparison and contrast should include only those details that will support your topic.

Comparing: A bus and a car both have wheels.
Contrasting: A bus is bigger than a car.
A bus holds more people than a car.

Read the topic for each paragraph. Then write the details that compare in the first column. Write the details that contrast in the second column.

1. Polly is going to write a paragraph about dogs and cats to show which animals make the best pets.

   dogs and cats are friendly
   cats can scratch
   dogs are noisier
   both animals are fun to have

   Compare

   a. dogs and cats are friendly

   b. both animals are fun to have

   Contrast

   a. cats can scratch

   b. dogs are noisier

2. Turner wants to write a paragraph that compares the Pacific Ocean and the Atlantic Ocean to give information about the two oceans.

   both have salt water
   the Atlantic Ocean is the most important ocean for trade
   the Pacific Ocean is larger
   ships travel on both the Atlantic and Pacific oceans

   Compare

   a. both have salt water

   b. ships travel on both the Atlantic and Pacific oceans

   Contrast

   a. the Atlantic Ocean is the most important ocean for trade

   b. the Pacific Ocean is larger

Name

Writer's Resources:
The Library

Fiction —→	books that contain made-up stories
	Winnie the Pooh
Nonfiction —→	books that contain facts and practical information
	The Story of Solar Energy
Reference —→	books of facts and practical information such as
	dictionaries, encyclopedias, atlases, and directories
	Webster's New Collegiate Dictionary

A. Circle the correct answer.

1. Which of these titles names a fiction book?

   The Complete Rhyming Dictionary   (*The Secret Garden*)

   An Introduction to Birds

2. Which of these books would be found on the nonfiction shelves?

   (*Americans in Space*)   *World Book Encyclopedia*

   The Adventures of Pinocchio

3. Which of these titles names a reference book?

   Charlotte's Web   *How to Be a Nature Detective*

   (*Century World Atlas*)

B. In which part of the library would you find each book? Write
   fiction, nonfiction, or **reference.**

4. *The Horse in the Attic* _____ fiction

5. *Encyclopedia Britannica* _____ reference

6. *The Kid in the Red Jacket* _____ fiction

7. *Bridges and How They Are Built* _____ nonfiction

8. *American Heritage Dictionary* _____ reference

9. *Sketching Outdoors in Spring* _____ nonfiction

10. *The Borrowers Aloft* _____ fiction

Macmillan LANGUAGE ARTS TODAY
Grade 4, Unit 4, Lesson 5, pages 142–143

Name

Writer's Resources:
The Card Catalog

The **card catalog** contains cards on all the books in the library. The cards are filed in alphabetical order. Each book is listed on a title card and on an author card. Every nonfiction book and some fiction books have a subject card, too. Each card has a **call number** in the upper left corner to help find the book.

```
                                    Title card
      363    The life of a fire fighter.
      B      Bester, Roger.
                The life of a fire fighter.
                New York : Crown Publishers, c1981.
                45 p. : illus.
```

Author card

```
      363    Bester, Roger.
      B         The life of a fire fighter.
                New York : Crown Publishers, c1981.
                45 p. : illus.
```

Subject card

```
      363    FIRE FIGHTING
      B      Bester, Roger.
                The life of a fire fighter.
                New York : Crown Publishers, c1981.
                45 p. : illus.
```

A. Use the sample catalog cards above to answer each question.

1. What is the title of the book? _____ The Life of a Fire Fighter

2. Who is the author of the book? _____ Roger Bester

3. In what year was the book published? _____ 1981

B. Underline the card that you would use to find each of the following books.

4. A book by Nancy Johnson   (subject, <u>author</u>, title)

5. A book called *Dogs at Work*   (subject, author, <u>title</u>)

6. A book about the weather   (<u>subject</u>, author, title)

Macmillan LANGUAGE ARTS TODAY
Grade 4, Unit 4, Lesson 6, pages 144–145

Name _____

What Is an Action Verb?

An **action verb** ⟶ is a verb that expresses action.
tells what the subject does or did.

Brian ⟶ { walks / skips / marched } ⟶ to the gym.

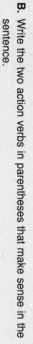

A. Underline each action verb.

1. Brian changed his clothes.
2. He put them into a locker.
3. The coach blows his whistle.
4. The boys run onto the basketball court.
5. The coach tosses them a ball.
6. Terry throws the ball to Chris.
7. Chris hurries down the court.
8. He jumped high.
9. Chris scored the first two points.

B. Write the two action verbs in parentheses that make sense in the sentence.

10. The boys (cheer, without, clap) for Chris.

_____ cheer _____ clap

11. Daniel (hits, always, taps) the ball.

_____ hits _____ taps

12. Steven (catches, people, grabs) the ball.

_____ catches _____ grabs

13. Quickly he (raced, zoomed, into) down the court.

_____ raced _____ zoomed

14. Steven (pushed, dunked, saw) the ball into the basket!

_____ pushed _____ dunked

Name _____

Main Verbs and Helping Verbs

The **main verb** is the most important verb. **A helping verb** is a verb that comes before the main verb.

helping main

A robin has built its nest in our tree.

Helping Verbs
am, is, are, was, were has, have, had, will

Read each sentence. Write the helping verb in the first column and the main verb in the second column.

1. I am watching the robin.

_____ am _____ watching

2. It has picked a spot on a big branch.

_____ has _____ picked

3. The robin's mate is helping with the nest.

_____ is _____ helping

4. They have found small twigs for the nest.

_____ have _____ found

5. The mother bird is putting the twigs in the nest.

_____ is _____ putting

6. They will use some mud for cement.

_____ will _____ use

7. The father bird is carrying a piece of red string.

_____ is _____ carrying

8. The string will make the nest pretty.

_____ will _____ make

9. The birds are working hard.

_____ are _____ working

10. Yesterday the rain had stopped the birds.

_____ had _____ stopped

RETEACHING·33

A **verb** can tell you when an action takes place. The **tense** of a verb tells you if something is happening in the present, in the past, or in the future. A **present tense** verb tells what happens now. A **past tense** verb tells what happened in the past. A **future tense** verb tells what will happen in the future. To write the future tense, use the special verb **will**.

Present Tense	Past Tense	Future Tense
work I work hard now.	worked I worked hard yesterday.	will work I will work hard tomorrow.

A. Write **present tense**, **past tense**, or **future tense** for each underlined verb.

1. I <u>wake</u> up each morning at six o'clock. _____ present tense

2. The alarm just <u>sits</u> beside my bed.
   I don't need it. _____ present tense

3. Yesterday something terrible <u>happened</u>. _____ past tense

4. My eyes <u>opened</u> at 7:30 A.M. _____ past tense

5. Now I <u>will set</u> my alarm every night. _____ future tense

B. Complete each sentence with a verb from the box that makes sense.

raises	learned	will own	worked	like

6. Last summer I **worked** _____ at my grandfather's ranch.

7. My grandfather **raises** _____ and sells horses.

8. I **like** _____ his ranch very much.

9. I **learned** _____ a lot about horses.

10. One day I **will own** _____ a ranch.

RETEACHING·34

Verbs in the **present tense** tell what happens now.
   Tom climbs trees.

Verbs in the **past tense** tell what happened in the past.
   Yesterday Tom climbed a tree.

Verbs in the **future tense** tell what will happen in the future.
(Use the special verb **will**.)
   Tomorrow Tom will climb another tree.

A. Circle the correct tense of the underlined verb.

1. Tom <u>runs</u> very fast. — (**present**) past future

2. He <u>chases</u> rabbits. — (**present**) past future

3. Yesterday Tom <u>watched</u> a spider. — present (**past**) future

4. He <u>touched</u> the spider gently. — present (**past**) future

5. He <u>will celebrate</u> his tenth birthday soon. — present past (**future**)

6. We <u>will give</u> him a special dinner. — present past (**future**)

7. He <u>likes</u> tuna very much. — (**present**) past future

8. Tom <u>gobbled</u> down a whole can yesterday. — present (**past**) future

9. He <u>will thank</u> us in his own way. — present past (**future**)

10. By the way, Tom <u>makes</u> a meow sound. — (**present**) past future

B. Underline the verb that makes sense in each sentence. Make sure the verb is in the correct tense.

11. Tom is my pet. I (brush, <u>brushed</u>) him every day.

12. His fur (looks, <u>will look</u>) so shiny right now.

13. Yesterday Tom (walks, <u>walked</u>) in some mud.

14. His coat (looks, <u>looked</u>) terrible yesterday.

15. In the future he (stayed, <u>will stay</u>) inside during rainy weather.

T17

Subject-Verb Agreement

A verb must **agree** with the subject of a sentence.

singular noun
he, she, or **it** ⟶ singular verb

Dad swims every morning.

Add **s** or **es** to make a verb singular.

plural noun
I, we, you, or **they** ⟶ plural verb

They swim every morning.

To make the verb plural, do **not** add **s** or **es.**

A. Write the verb in parentheses that completes each sentence.

1. My parents _____ hard on Saturdays. (work, works) work

2. Dad _____ his car once a month. (wax, waxes) waxes

3. He also _____ the attic and garage. (clean, cleans) cleans

4. Mom _____ my grandparents. (visit, visits) visits

5. She _____ homemade muffins to them. (take, takes) takes

B. Write the correct form of the verb in parentheses.

6. Uncle Davis _____ unusual kites. (make, makes) makes

7. Children _____ his kites to the park. (take, takes) take

8. Suddenly dragons _____ through the sky. (soar, soars) soar

9. Parents _____ them go higher and higher. (watch, watches) watch

10. Two kites _____ by the flagpole. (pass, passes) pass

Using Irregular Verbs I

You can form the past tense of most verbs by adding the letters **ed** to the verb.
Verbs that do not add **ed** to form the past tense are called **irregular verbs.**

Present	Past	Past with has, have, or had
come	came	has, have, or had come
drive	drove	has, have, or had driven
eat	ate	has, have, or had eaten
give	gave	has, have, or had given
go	went	has, have, or had gone
ride	rode	has, have, or had ridden
run	ran	has, have, or had run
see	saw	has, have, or had seen
write	wrote	has, have, or had written

A. Underline the correct form of the verb in the past tense that completes each sentence.

1. My grandfather (drive, drove) a fire truck for many years.

2. Once I (rode, ride) in the fire truck with him.

3. I (see, saw) all the things inside the truck.

4. I (went, go) with Grandfather during a parade.

5. Many people (came, come) to the parade.

B. Circle the correct form of the verb.

6. I have (gone, went) to the fire station many times.

7. Mom has (came, come) with me a few times.

8. She has (drove, driven) me there in her car.

9. I have (ate, eaten) a few meals at the fire station.

10. I have (seen, saw) the cook in the kitchen.

Using Irregular Verbs II

RETEACHING·37

You can form the past tense of most verbs by adding the letters **ed** to the verb.

Verbs that do not add **ed** to form the past tense are called irregular verbs.

Present	Past	Past with has, have, or had
bring	brought	has, have, or had brought
do	did	has, have, or had done
draw	drew	has, have, or had drawn
fly	flew	has, have, or had flown
grow	grew	has, have, or had grown
make	made	has, have, or had made
sing	sang	has, have, or had sung
swim	swam	has, have, or had swum
take	took	has, have, or had taken
throw	threw	has, have, or had thrown

A. Underline the correct form of the verb in the past tense.

1. Last Saturday my family (did, do) many things.
2. Matt (fly, flew) in a helicopter.
3. Janice (swim, swam) in a swimming meet.
4. My mom (sang, sing) in a concert.
5. Dad (draw, drew) a picture of me.

B. Circle the correct form of the verb in parentheses.

6. My family has (took, taken) several vacations in Florida.
7. We have (bring, brought) our dog Digger with us.
8. Dad has (thrown, threw) a ball into the ocean.
9. Digger has (swim, swum) after it.
10. Digger has (make, made) us all laugh.

Spelling Verbs Correctly

RETEACHING·38

Some verbs add **s** to form the **present tense.** ——▸ wait = waits

Many verbs add **ed** to form the **past tense.** ——▸ wait = waited

Spelling Rules for Adding es or ed to Some Verbs

- Change the **y** to **i** before adding **es** or **ed** to verbs that end with a consonant and **y.** ——▸ carry = carries and carried
- Double the final consonant and add **es** or **ed** to verbs that end with one vowel and one consonant. ——▸ trim = trimmed
- Drop the **e** and add **es** or **ed** to verbs that end in **e.** close = closes and closed

A. Underline the correct present-tense or past-tense form of the verb in parentheses.

1. Pete (tryed, tried) to earn some money last week.   past
2. He (carried, carryed) 50 empty bottles back to the store.   past
3. The clerk (grined, grinned) at him.   past
4. "Where were the bottles (stored, storeed)?" the clerk asked.   past
5. "I (dropped, droped) them in bags in the basement," Pete answered.   past
6. The clerk (emptys, empties) a lot of change into Pete's hand.   present
7. He (studies, studys) the change in his hand.   present
8. Then he (charges, chargees) out the door to the nearby video store.   present
9. That afternoon he (invites, invitees) his friends over to see a movie.   present

B. Write the correct past-tense form of the verb in parentheses.

10. I have (flip) through this catalog ten times.   _____ flipped
11. I had (worry) about the math test, but I did well.   _____ worried
12. I haven't (notice) the right things yet.   _____ noticed

Name _____

Mechanics:
Using the Comma

When you speak, you pause between words. In writing, **commas** show a reader where to pause. Use commas (,):

- after each word in a **series** except the last word.
  Mercury, Venus, and Earth are the closest planets to the sun.
- to set off a person's name when the person is being directly addressed.
  Terry, did you know that Mercury is the smallest planet?
- after the words **yes, no,** and **well.**
  Yes, the earth is three times bigger than Mercury.

Rewrite each sentence. Use commas where they are needed.

1. There are big rocks craters and mountains on Venus.
   There are big rocks, craters, and mountains on Venus.

2. Yes Venus is the closest planet to Earth.
   Yes, Venus is the closest planet to Earth.

3. Mrs. Morgan could there be life on Venus?
   Mrs. Morgan, could there be life on Venus?

4. No life cannot exist on Venus.
   No, life cannot exist on Venus.

5. On Mars you would find red dust ice and strong winds.
   On Mars you would find red dust, ice, and strong winds.

6. Victor how many moons does Mars have?
   Victor, how many moons does Mars have?

7. Well I read that it has two moons.
   Well, I read that it has two moons.

8. Jupiter has 16 moons a rocky surface and a red spot.
   Jupiter has 16 moons, a rocky surface, and a red spot.

Name _____

Vocabulary Building:
Prefixes

A **prefix** is a word part added to the beginning of a word. A **base word** is a word to which a prefix is added. A prefix changes the meaning of a base word.

Prefix	Meaning		Example	
dis	not, opposite of		dislike	(not like)
im	not, without		immovable	(not movable)
in	not, without		insecure	(not secure)
un	not, opposite of		unwanted	(not wanted)
non	not, opposite of, without		nonstop	(not stopping)
mis	incorrectly		misplace	(place incorrectly)
pre	before		prepaid	(paid before)
re	again, back		restate	(state again)

To figure out the meaning of a word, put together the meaning of the prefix and the meaning of the base word.

A. Write the letter of the meaning of each word.

__d__ 1. misjudge   a. heat again

__e__ 2. pretest   b. not fiction

__a__ 3. reheat   c. not loyal

__b__ 4. nonfiction   d. judge incorrectly

__c__ 5. disloyal   e. test before

B. Write a sentence using each word. Use the prefix as a clue to the meaning of the word. (Answers will vary.)

6. unhappy
   She was unhappy because her dog ran away.

7. impossible
   It is impossible to cross the ocean by bicycle.

8. dishonest
   He was dishonest because he didn't tell you the truth.

9. unable
   I am unable to finish this job without your help.

10. imbalance
    The imbalance will make the scale tip to one side.

Name _____

Grammar and Writing Connection:
Making Subjects and Verbs Agree

Be sure that subjects and verbs agree in sentences. In sentences with helping verbs, the helping verb in each sentence must also agree with the subject. **Has, have,** and **had** are helping verbs.

Use **has** with a singular subject.

My sister has seen the gymnastic team perform.

Use **have** with plural subjects and I and **you**.

The people have seen the gymnastic team perform.
I have seen the gymnastic team perform.

Use **had** with singular or plural subjects.

The man had seen the gymnastic team perform.
The men had seen the gymnastic team perform.

A. Underline the helping verb that correctly completes each sentence.

1. Children of all ages (have, has) come to swimming class.
2. Sara (has, had) started swimming when she was five years old.
3. Her brothers (have, has) always enjoyed swimming.
4. They (has, have) helped her learn how to swim well.
5. In one exercise, you (has, have) to practice kicking in the water.
6. Swimming (have, has) made Sara strong.

B. Write the helping verb **has, have,** or **had** to complete the following sentences. (Answers will vary.)

7. About 500,000 young people across the United States _____ practiced gymnastics.   have, had

8. A gold medal _____ always been a goal in the Olympics.   has, had

9. I _____ wanted to watch gymnastics during the Olympics.   had, have

10. My friends _____ joined a gymnastics club.   had, have

Name _____

Group Writing:
A Friendly Letter

A **friendly letter** must have a **purpose** and an **audience.** The correct form of a **friendly letter** has five parts:

• The **heading** includes your address and the date.
• The **greeting** usually includes the word *dear,* followed by the name of the person to whom you are writing.
• The **body** includes everything that you want to say.
• The **closing** is a way to say "good-bye," such as "Your friend."
• The **signature** is your name, written under the closing.

Think of two events that happened to you last week. Write a letter to a friend or relative and tell that person your news. (Answers will vary.)

_____ } heading

_____ } greeting

_____
_____
_____
_____ } body
_____

_____ } closing

_____ } signature

T21

Thinking and Writing:
Solving Problems

RETEACHING·43

To **solve a problem**, it helps to have a plan that includes the following steps:

- State what the problem is.
- State a possible solution.
- List the steps to follow to solve the problem.

Problem	Solution	Steps to Follow
What to do for Mom's birthday	Make her a card.	1. Get paper and crayons. 2. Fold and decorate the paper. 3. Write a note inside.

Underline the solution for each of the following problems. Then circle the steps to follow to reach that solution.

1. Problem: How to do well on the baseball team

Solution:
a. Sit in the stands and watch the game.
b. Score runs in the next game.

Steps:
Practice hitting.　　Watch television.

Practice cheering.

2. Problem: How to find Jefferson Avenue

Solution:
a. Use a map.
b. Take a walk.

Steps:
Have lunch.　　Go shopping.

Get a map of the area.　　Find where you are and where you want to be on the map.

3. Problem: What to wear to school

Solution:
a. Check the weather.
b. Check the date.

Steps:
Look out the window.　　Listen to the radio.

Eat breakfast.　　Do homework.

Macmillan LANGUAGE ARTS TODAY
Grade 4, Unit 6, Lesson 2, pages 204–205

Writer's Resources:
Parts of a Book

RETEACHING·44

A book is often divided into parts. Knowing the purpose of each part can help you find information.

Front of a book

- The **title page** is the first page of the book. It tells the title, the author, and the publisher of the book.
- The **copyright page** is after the title page. It tells the date the book was published.
- The **table of contents** lists the chapters and page numbers.

The **body** of a book is the main part of the book. It contains all the parts listed in the table of contents.

Back of a book

- The **glossary** defines special words used in the book.
- The **index** is after the glossary. It lists topics alphabetically and page numbers where the topics can be found in the book.

A. Beside each number, write the letter of the part of the book each student should use to find the information.

a. Title page
b. copyright page
c. index
d. glossary

a ___ **1.** Tony wants to know the name of the person who wrote the book she is reading.

c ___ **2.** Erick wants to know which pages in his science book tell about clouds.

b ___ **3.** Sue wants to know in what year her reading book was published.

d ___ **4.** Carlos wants to know the meaning of the word *tropical*.

B. Use your textbook to answer the following questions.

5. On which page does Unit 11 begin? ___ 356

6. Who is the publisher of this book? ___ Macmillan Publishing Company

7. On what page does the *Thesaurus for Writing* begin? ___ 499

Macmillan LANGUAGE ARTS TODAY
Grade 4, Unit 6, Lesson 5, pages 216–217

What Is a Linking Verb?

RETEACHING·45

An **action verb** tells what the subject does or did.

My cat plays with yarn.

A **linking verb** links the subject of a sentence to a noun or adjective in the predicate. A linking verb does not express action.

My cat is playful.

The words **am, is, are, was,** and **were** are important linking verbs. They are forms of the verb **be.**

My cat is a tabby.   Her stripes are gray.

A. Write whether each underlined verb is an **action verb** or a **linking verb.**

1. My cat's name is Fluffy. _____ linking verb
2. She purrs a lot. _____ action verb
3. Her paws are all white. _____ linking verb
4. She always cleans her fur. _____ action verb
5. Her fur is very soft. _____ linking verb

B. Underline each verb. Write whether it is an **action verb** or a **linking verb.**

6. Muffin sits by the window every day. _____ action verb
7. She watches the people and cars. _____ action verb
8. Her favorite food is fish. _____ linking verb
9. But all of her food disappears quickly. _____ action verb
10. I am her cook. _____ linking verb
11. She gobbles every bit of her food. _____ action verb
12. Her plate is very clean. _____ linking verb
13. Fluffy sleeps on my bed. _____ action verb
14. I am a lucky person. _____ linking verb

Linking Verbs in the Present Tense

RETEACHING·46

Am, is, and **are** are present tense linking verbs. A linking verb must agree with the subject of a sentence. Subjects can be singular or plural.

Subject	Linking Verb
I	am

I am enjoying the book.

she, he, it, or singular noun——→ **is**
She is laughing at the funny story.

you, we, they, or plural noun——→ **are**
They are reading the same book.

compound subject (two or more things)——→ **are**
Both books are well written.

A. Write the correct form of the linking verb in the present tense.

1. This book (is, are) very interesting. _____ is
2. It (is, are) about music. _____ is
3. You (is, are) a good piano player. _____ are
4. I (is, am) a fairly good drummer. _____ am
5. Beth and Linda (is, are) good singers. _____ are
6. They (is, are) wonderful when they sing together. _____ are

B. Draw a line to connect each subject on the left with a predicate on the right. Use the correct linking verb in the present tense.

7. An orchestra — are proud of her.
8. Betsy — am a member of her orchestra.
9. I — is a large group of musicians.
10. Betsy's mom and dad — is an orchestra leader.

Linking Verbs in the Past Tense

Remember that the subject of a sentence can be singular or plural and that a linking verb must agree with the subject of a sentence. **Was** and **were** are past tense linking verbs. Different subjects go with the different verbs.

Subject		Linking Verb
I, she, he, it, or singular noun		
He was at the baseball game yesterday.	→	**was**
you, we, they, or plural noun		
They were at the baseball game, too.	→	**were**
compound subject (two or more things)	→	**were**
My friends and my family were both at the same baseball game.		

A. Write the correct form of the linking verb in the past tense.

1. I (was, were) in third grade last year. _____ was
2. Paul and Elroy (was, were) my best friends. _____ were
3. They (was, were) also my next-door neighbors. _____ were
4. Mrs. McGregor (was, were) my teacher. _____ was
5. She (was, were) very nice. _____ was

B. Draw a line to connect each subject on the left with a predicate on the right. Use the correct linking verb in the past tense.

6. Franklin School .... was Mr. Valentine.
7. The teachers .... were built a few years ago.
8. My principal .... were friendly.
9. My mother .... was my school last year.
10. A new gym and playground .... was once a student at Franklin School.

Using Linking Verbs

When you write, be sure the subject of your sentence agrees with the verb. **Am, is,** and **are** are present tense linking verbs. **Was** and **were** are past tense linking verbs.

Subject		Linking Verb
I		
I am at the library today.		
I was at the library yesterday.	→	**am and was**
she, he, it, or singular noun		
He is at the library now.		
She was at the library before.	→	**is and was**
you, we, they, or plural noun		
Today we are at the library together.		
Last week we were at home.	→	**are and were**
compound subject (two or more things)	→	**are and were**
The books and magazines are on the shelves.		
The records and films were there last week.		

A. Write the correct linking verb in parentheses.

1. David (is, are) _____ is _____ an artist.
2. His pictures (is, are) _____ are _____ beautiful.
3. Blue, yellow, and red (was, were) _____ were _____ his main colors.
4. He (was, were) _____ was _____ delighted with the results.
5. I (is, am) _____ am _____ an admirer of fine art.

B. Underline the correct linking verb in parentheses.

6. Mr. and Mrs. Henderson (was, were) our neighbors.
7. They (was, were) very nice.
8. Now the house next door (is, are) empty.
9. We (is, are) sad.

Name

Contractions with not

A **contraction** is a shortened form of two words. An **apostrophe** (') takes the place of one or more letters that are left out.

is not → i s ☐ n ☐o☐ t → isn ☐'☐ t → isn't

is not → isn't	was not → wasn't	
are not → aren't	were not → weren't	
has not → hasn't	do not → don't	
have not → haven't	could not → couldn't	

A. Write the contraction for each pair of words.

1. should not ___ shouldn't
2. have not ___ haven't
3. was not ___ wasn't
4. did not ___ didn't
5. are not ___ aren't

6. can not ___ can't
7. is not ___ isn't
8. were not ___ weren't
9. has not ___ hasn't
10. would not ___ wouldn't

B. Write the two words that make up each contraction in parentheses.

11. I (don't) ___ do not ___ remember his name.
12. It (isn't) ___ is not ___ Thomas.
13. It (couldn't) ___ could not ___ be Gregory.
14. William and Jeffrey (aren't) ___ are not ___ even close.
15. I (haven't) ___ have not ___ the slightest idea what his name is.

Name

Mechanics: Using Quotation Marks

When you write a speaker's exact words, it is called a **direct quotation**. Use **quotation marks** before and after a direct quotation.

- Use quotation marks to show a speaker's exact words.

  "Every beehive has one queen bee," Mrs. Hines said.

- Never use quotation marks around the words that tell who is speaking.

  "Some hives have as many as 8,000 bees," she added.

- Do not use quotation marks when you do not use the speaker's exact words.

  Nora said that the queen lays all the eggs.

A. Rewrite each sentence. Add quotation marks where they belong.

1. Worker bees also clean the hive, Mrs. Hines added.

   "Worker bees also clean the hive," Mrs. Hines added.

2. Soon grubs hatch from the eggs, she said.

   "Soon grubs hatch from the eggs," she said.

3. Nora commented, The grubs are very hungry.

   Nora commented, "The grubs are very hungry."

4. The worker bees must feed them, Jeff responded.

   "The worker bees must feed them," Jeff responded.

B. Read each sentence. Write **correct** next to each sentence that uses quotation marks correctly.

5. "Older worker bees go outside the hive," Mrs. Hines added. ___ Correct

6. She told us "that worker bees look for nectar and pollen."

7. "Bees make honey from flower nectar," Nora added. ___ Correct

8. "Mrs. Hines said," the bees keep the honey in a honeycomb. ___

T25

Vocabulary Building:
Suffixes

A **suffix** is a word part that is added to the end of a base word. A suffix changes the meaning of the base word to which it is added.

Suffix	Meaning	Example
able (ible)	capable of, liable to	readable (capable of being read)
er (or)	one who does, that which does	worker (one who works)
ful	full of	powerful (full of power)
less	without	weightless (without weight)
ly	in the manner of, slowly (in a slow manner)	
ment	result	retirement (result of being retired)
y	having, being like	rainy (having rain)

A. Write the letter of the meaning that fits each word.

___ **1.** breakable   **a.** result of being punished

___ **2.** owner   **b.** one who owns

___ **3.** guilty   **c.** capable of being broken

___ **4.** punishment   **d.** having guilt

___ **5.** lawless   **e.** without any law

___ **6.** sisterly   **f.** full of hope

___ **7.** hopeful   **g.** in the manner of a sister

B. Write a sentence for each word. Use the suffix as a clue to the meaning of the word. (Answers will vary.)

8. salty

The ocean is very salty.

9. fearful

We were fearful that the rain would leak through the roof.

10. valueless

The jeweler said that the ring was valueless.

11. gardener

Those roses were planted by a gardener.

12. normally

We normally eat dinner at six o'clock.

Grammar and Writing Connection:
Combining Sentences

Sometimes sentences have related ideas. When ideas in separate sentences are related, you can join them to make one sentence. Use the word **and** or **but.**

My grandparents [own a ranch.]

My grandparents [own a ranch and raise horses.]

My grandparents [raise horses.]

Write each pair of sentences as one sentence by joining the predicates with the word in parentheses.

1. Grandmother meets new workers. She hires them. (and)

Grandmother meets and hires new workers.

2. Grandfather assigns the chores. He helps the workers. (and)

Grandfather assigns the chores and helps the workers.

3. Each summer I visit them. I can only stay at the ranch for two weeks. (but)

Each summer I visit them but can only stay at the ranch for two weeks.

4. I help with the horses. I work for free. (but)

I help with the horses but work for free.

5. The workers clean out the stalls. They put fresh hay in them. (and)

The workers clean out the stalls and put fresh hay in them.

6. I ride most of the horses. I avoid Big Red. (but)

I ride most of the horses but avoid Big Red.

7. Big Red runs very fast. He jumps tall fences. (and)

Big Red runs very fast and jumps tall fences.

8. I work hard at the ranch. I enjoy myself very much. (but)

I work hard at the ranch but enjoy myself very much.

Group Writing:
A Story

A story should be entertaining and fun to read. It should have:

- interesting **characters** and **setting**.
  The **characters** are the people in the story. The **main character** is the most important character. The **setting** is where and when the story takes place.

- a good **beginning, middle,** and **end.**
  The **beginning** introduces the characters, the setting, and the **plot,** or the events of the story. The main character faces a problem. In the **middle,** the plot is developed. The main character faces a problem. The **end** tells how the problem is solved.

- a logical **sequence** of events.
  The events in a story often occur in time order.

A. Write whether each item names a **character, setting,** or **problem.**

1. the Kindalls' farm hasn't had rain for two months _____ problem

2. the next king of England _____ character

3. a small island in the Pacific Ocean _____ setting

4. an Eskimo village in Alaska _____ setting

B. Think of a story you have read or would like to write. Answer these questions about the story. (Answers will vary.)

5. What is the setting? _____

6. Who is the main character? _____

7. What is the problem that the main character has? _____

8. What is one way the main character might try to solve the problem? _____

9. How does the story finally end? _____

Thinking and Writing:
Understanding Sequence

A story's sequence of events should move logically from the beginning through the middle to the end. Events in a story are usually arranged in time order.

Number the events of each plot from 1 to 7 to show the correct sequence, or time order.

1. Setting: Simpson Street Elementary School
Main Character: Bryan O'Leary
Plot:

- 7   Bryan calls his mother and asks her to bring him a clean shirt.
- 1   Bryan gets the box of paints out of the closet in the art room.
- 2   He gets brown paint on his shirt as he is painting a tree.
- 4   He takes off his shirt and hangs it up to dry.
- 3   He tries to wash off the brown paint, but the spot gets bigger.
- 5   Patsy thinks Bryan's shirt is a rag and throws it into the rag pile.
- 6   Bryan can't find his shirt.

2. Setting: the imaginary planet Placroton
Main Character: Captain Jake Rawlings
Plot:

- 3   Captain Rawlings lands on Placroton.
- 5   He digs up the two plants and places them in jars.
- 1   Captain Rawlings blasts off from Earth.
- 4   While exploring Placroton he discovers two unusual plants.
- 2   He avoids being hit by meteorites during the flight to Placroton.
- 7   Earth scientists discover that the plants have medicinal qualities.
- 6   Captain Rawlings returns to Earth with the plants.

Writer's Resources: The Thesaurus

A **thesaurus** is a reference book that gives synonyms and antonyms for many words.

Synonyms are words that have the same or almost the same meaning.
Antonyms are words that have an opposite meaning.

The following is a sample entry from a thesaurus.

NEW—(*adj.*) modern, recent, advanced, fresh, unused, unknown, beginning, different

The word *new* in the sentence below may be replaced by a synonym for that word from the thesaurus entry.

Amy has a <u>new</u> typewriter.   Amy has a <u>modern</u> typewriter.

A. Use the sample entry to answer the following questions.

1. Would the word *old* be a synonym or an antonym for the word *new?*
   antonym

2. How many synonyms are given for the word *new?* 8

3. Is *new* used as a noun or an adjective? _adjective_

4. What are two synonyms for *new?* _fresh, beginning (Answers will vary.)_

5. Would the words *aged* or *out-of-date* be synonyms or antonyms for the word *new?* _antonyms_

B. For each sentence, circle the synonym that best fits the meaning of the underlined word.

6. This <u>new</u> head of lettuce is crisp. (recent, unused,(fresh))

7. This is a <u>new</u> box of cereal. (modern,(unused,) beginning)

8. My father works in that <u>new</u> building. ((modern,) fresh, unknown)

9. That girl is a <u>new</u> student. (advanced,(unknown,) fresh)

10. I have a <u>new</u> address now. (advanced, beginning,(different))

What Is an Adjective?

Adjectives ← are words that describe nouns.
can tell **what kind** or **how many.**
usually come before the nouns they describe.

red flower   old house   wet shoes
bright light   cold wind   tall hat

A. Circle the adjective that describes each underlined noun.

1. The animal with the (longest) <u>nose</u> is the elephant.

2. The elephant is a (strong) <u>animal.</u>

3. The trunk of the elephant has (many) <u>uses.</u>

4. With its trunk, an elephant drinks (cool) <u>water.</u>

5. A (dirty) elephant cleans itself with water from its trunk.

B. Underline the adjective in each sentence. Write the noun the adjective describes.

6. An elephant can pick up a small berry with its trunk. _____ berry

7. It can also pull up a huge tree out of the ground. _____ tree

8. Elephants do not eat meat; they eat things like green leaves. _____ leaves

9. Elephants are smart animals. _____ animals

10. They have been trained to be excellent helpers. _____ helpers

11. They can easily move heavy objects. _____ objects

12. Elephants live together in large groups. _____ groups

13. People have killed elephants for their shiny tusks. _____ tusks

14. Strict laws now protect elephants. _____ laws

15. Elephants live for many years. _____ years

Adjectives After Linking Verbs

Sometimes an adjective **follows** the noun it describes. When an adjective follows the noun it describes, the noun and adjective are connected by a linking verb. The linking verb is usually a form of the verb *be*.

Summer is wonderful.   The days are long.

The temperatures are warm.

A. Circle the adjective that describes each underlined noun.

1. <u>Sports</u> in the summer are (fun).
2. The pool's <u>water</u> is (cool).
3. <u>Food</u> on the grill is (delicious).
4. <u>Chicken</u> is (tasty) when cooked on a grill.
5. In the summer, <u>people</u> are (happy).

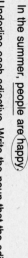

B. Underline each adjective. Write the noun that the adjective describes.

6. That rainbow is beautiful. _____ rainbow
7. The colors are bright. _____ colors
8. The sky is dark. _____ sky
9. The rain was heavy. _____ rain
10. The day was dreary. _____ day

C. Complete each sentence. Write an adjective that makes sense. (Answers will vary.)

11. I am _____ happy .
12. My home is _____ new .
13. My family is _____ friendly .
14. My friend is _____ kind .
15. School is _____ fun .

Adjectives That Compare

Adjectives that compare nouns often end in **er** or **est**.

- Adjective + **er** ⟶ compares two nouns.

  A cheetah is faster than a leopard.

- Adjective + **est** ⟶ compares more than two nouns.

  The giraffe is the <u>tallest</u> mammal in the world.

A. Underline the correct form of the adjective in parentheses.

1. The giraffe's neck can be 20 feet long. It has the (longer, <u>longest</u>) neck in the animal kingdom.
2. An ostrich's neck is $4\frac{1}{4}$ feet long. A flamingo's neck is $3\frac{1}{4}$ feet long. The ostrich's neck is (longer, longest) than the flamingo's neck.
3. The cheetah can run at a speed of 71 miles per hour. It is the (faster, fastest) animal in the world.
4. To go one mile, a snail needs 13 days. To go one mile, a tortoise needs about $4\frac{1}{2}$ hours. The snail is (slower, slowest) than the tortoise.
5. An ostrich egg weighs about $3\frac{1}{4}$ pounds. It is the (bigger, biggest) egg in the world.

B. Write the correct form of the adjective in parentheses.

6. This is the (bigger, biggest) book on planets that I have ever seen. _____ biggest
7. Did you know that Venus is the (brighter, brightest) planet in the solar system? _____ brightest
8. Jupiter is the (bigger, biggest) planet of all. _____ biggest
9. Venus is (closer, closest) to the sun than Mars. _____ closer
10. I'm (smarter, smartest) now than I was before I read this book. _____ smarter

Spelling Adjectives That Compare

RETEACHING·59

When adding **er** or **est** to adjectives, follow these spelling rules:

- If an adjective ends with **e**, drop the **e** before adding **er** or **est**.

little	littler	littlest

- If an adjective ends with a consonant and **y**, change the **y** to **i** and add **er** or **est**.

heavy	heavier	heaviest

- If a one-syllable adjective ends with a consonant-vowel-consonant, double the final consonant before adding **er** or **est**.

flat	flatter	flattest

A. Add the endings **er** and **est** to each adjective in the list. Then write the new words on the lines.

	er	est
1. pretty	prettier	prettiest
2. hot	hotter	hottest
3. wide	wider	widest
4. safe	safer	safest
5. happy	happier	happiest

B. Write the correct **er** or **est** form of the adjective in parentheses.

6. (heavy)   Which is _____ heavier _____, a ton of rocks or a ton of sand?

7. (silly)   That is the _____ silliest _____ joke I have heard all day.

8. (funny)   Actually, that is a _____ funnier _____ joke than the one you told me yesterday.

9. (hard)   Your jokes are _____ harder _____ to guess than they were last year.

10. (witty)   I think they are the _____ wittiest _____ jokes I have ever heard.

Comparing with more and most

RETEACHING·60

Use **more** and **most** with most adjectives that have two or more syllables.

- To compare two nouns ____→ **more** + adjective

  This camera is _more_ reliable than that camera.

- To compare more than two nouns ____→ **most** + adjective

  This camera is the _most_ reliable camera in the store.

Never use **more** or **most** with an adjective that already has an **er** or **est** ending.

  This camera is ~~more~~ smaller than that camera.

  This camera is the ~~most~~ smallest camera in the store.

A. Write the correct form of the adjective in parentheses.

1. The $140 camera is (more, most) powerful than the $38 camera. _____ more

2. This camera is (more, most) practical than that one because it fits in your pocket. _____ more

3. The camera that is on sale takes the (more, most) beautiful pictures of any camera in the store. _____ most

4. However, the small red camera is the (more, most) popular camera among young people. _____ most

B. Underline the correct form of the adjective in parentheses.

5. Today is the (most coldest, coldest) day of the year so far.

6. The snow is the (deepest, more deepest) I have ever seen.

7. The skies are (more darker, darker) than they were earlier.

8. I can't wait until it gets (more hotter, hotter) than it is today!

Using Articles

The words **a, an,** and **the** are special adjectives called **articles.**

- Use **a** before a singular noun that begins with a consonant.
  <u>a</u> chair   <u>a</u> table

- Use **an** before a singular noun that begins with a vowel.
  <u>an</u> arrow   <u>an</u> otter

- Use **the** before a singular noun that names a particular person, place, or thing.
  <u>the</u> deck   <u>the</u> map

- Use **the** before all plural nouns.   <u>the</u> dogs   <u>the</u> stores

A. Underline each article. Then write the noun that follows each article.

1. Dinosaurs were on <u>the</u> earth about 140 million years ago. _____ earth

2. Stripes on <u>a</u> zebra help it hide from its enemies. _____ zebra

3. <u>An</u> anteater actually eats ants. _____ anteater

4. Wolves in <u>the</u> United States live in packs. _____ United States

5. <u>A</u> horse can weigh as much as 2,000 pounds. _____ horse

6. At birth <u>a</u> giraffe is 6½ feet tall. _____ giraffe

7. <u>The</u> ostrich uses its long, powerful toes for defense. _____ ostrich

8. <u>An</u> elephant often pets her baby with her trunk. _____ elephant

B. Complete each sentence with the article **a** or **an.**

9. _____<u>A</u>_____ skunk can squirt out oil from glands near its tail.

10. The spray stings and burns _____<u>an</u>_____ animal's face.

11. It also has _____<u>a</u>_____ taste that is terrible.

12. The spray protects the skunk from _____<u>an</u>_____ enemy.

Mechanics: Capitalizing
Proper Adjectives

A **proper adjective** ⎯⎯ refers to a particular person, place, or thing. is always capitalized.

| Europe ⟶ | European ⟶ | European cities |
| North America ⟶ | North American ⟶ | North American coast |

Underline each proper adjective. Then write the noun each proper adjective describes.

1. I have read a lot about <u>American</u> history. _____ history

2. Leif Ericsson may have been the first <u>European</u> person to come to the Americas. _____ person

3. Christopher Columbus was an <u>Italian</u> citizen. _____ citizen

4. But, he sailed to America for the <u>Spanish</u> queen. _____ queen

5. Columbus actually wanted to get <u>Asian</u> goods. _____ goods

6. Columbus never landed on <u>North American</u> soil. _____ soil

7. A <u>German</u> man who made maps named the Americas after Amerigo Vespucci, an explorer. _____ man

8. Early <u>Spanish</u> explorers discovered Mexico and other parts of North and Central America. _____ explorers

9. Cortés, for example, discovered the city that is now the <u>Mexican</u> capital. _____ capital

10. After coming ashore on the <u>Panamanian</u> coast, Balboa climbed a mountain and discovered the Pacific Ocean. _____ coast

11. Heading south, Pizarro explored the <u>South American</u> continent and found the Inca Indians. _____ continent

12. In 1520, a <u>Portuguese</u> navigator named Magellan landed in what is now Argentina. _____ navigator

Name _____

Vocabulary Building:
Synonyms and Antonyms

Synonyms are words that have the same meaning or almost the same meaning.

tidy/neat	fast/quick	small/tiny

Antonyms are words that have opposite meanings.

tidy/messy	fast/slow	kind/unkind

Some antonyms can be formed by adding the prefix **un**.

able = unable   happy = unhappy

A. Circle the word in parentheses that is a **synonym** for the underlined word.

1. When I am in a play, I get <u>nervous</u>. (calm, (jumpy), nice)

2. My stomach feels funny, and my heart starts to beat fast. (stop, (pound), hit)

3. My mind goes <u>blank</u>, and I can't remember my lines. (dizzy, (empty), full)

4. But when the curtain goes up, I feel <u>fearless</u>. ((brave), cowardly, faint)

5. Plays I have been in have all been <u>successful</u>. (short, worthless, (rewarding))

B. Circle the word in parentheses that is an **antonym** for the underlined word.

6. Last Saturday I went upstairs into our <u>dreary</u> attic. (dark, dull, (bright))

7. I first spotted a <u>sturdy</u> old trunk. (strong, strange, (weak))

8. When I opened it, I smelled an <u>unpleasant</u> odor. ((pleasant), terrible, unlikeable)

9. It was only the musty smell of <u>old</u> books. (ancient, (new), used)

10. Inside the trunk was a <u>beautiful</u> picture of my mother as a young girl. (handsome, (ugly), boring)

Name _____

Grammar and Writing Connection:
Choosing Vivid Adjectives

A **vivid adjective** is one that makes your word picture very clear.

That restaurant has <u>good</u> food.

That restaurant has <u>tasty</u> food. more precise

A. Write the adjective in parentheses that is more exact.

1. Last night we ate at a restaurant with a (spectacular, nice) __spectacular__ view.

2. We could see a (pretty, blazing) __blazing__ sunset.

3. We were seated at a (clean, spotless) __spotless__ table.

4. A (charming, nice) __charming__ waiter gave us menus.

5. I ordered some (good, spicy) __spicy__ Italian food.

6. We all enjoyed our (delicious, nice) __delicious__ dinners.

7. Then the waiter brought us (huge, big) __huge__ desserts.

8. The (sweet, good) __sweet__ desserts quickly vanished.

9. The restaurant played (soft, pleasant) __soft__ dinner music.

10. Everyone had a (fine, wonderful) __wonderful__ time.

B. Write a colorful, vivid adjective on each blank line. (Answers will vary.)

11. The __annual__ fair was an __exciting__ event.

12. __Local__ musicians played their instruments before __friendly__ crowds.

13. The __mouth-watering__ aroma of food drifted through the tents.

14. __Proud__ owners led their animals before the judges.

15. By eight o'clock, __weary__ people headed toward their homes.

Name

Group Writing:
A Description

The **purpose** of a description is to create a clear and vivid picture. The following help make a picture clear and vivid for the audience:

- An Overall Impression → the general idea
- Sensory Details → tell more about how things look, sound, taste, feel, or smell
- Logical Order → details arranged in an order that is logical

A. Read the sentence and think about what the writer was trying to describe. Then write a sensory detail sentence that uses each of the following words. (Answers will vary.)

As we hiked slowly through the woods, we were awed by nature's many beautiful masterpieces.

silky	We touched the silky leaves of plants.
spicy	The orange berries on the berry bushes had a spicy smell.
prickly	We didn't get too close to one bush because of its prickly thorns.
rushing	We could hear the rushing water in the icy stream.

B. Arrange the details below in a logical order.

2 Then she looked out the window and saw snow.

5 Her mother had breakfast waiting for her.

8 Finally, Sue got her books and went to school.

1 First, Sue turned the alarm clock off and got out of bed.

4 After she got dressed, Sue went to the kitchen.

6 When she finished breakfast, Sue got her coat.

7 Then she put on her boots.

3 Sue knew she had better put on some warm clothes.

Name

Thinking and Writing:
Classifying Sensory Details

When you write a **description** you will have to decide which details are important. Include **details** that tell more about the overall impression.

My father painted my room. → overall impression
It is a light blue color.
The walls are wet.
The paint smells strong. → important details

I went to play baseball. → details that do not add
We ate chicken for dinner. → to the overall impression

A. Read each idea for a description. Then underline the details that should be included.

1. Raymond is going to write a description of the greenhouse his father owns. He wants to create an overall impression of the greenhouse as a wonderful place to work.

lovely flowers growing everywhere   very hot and humid
hands always in dirt and fertilizer   lots of cheerful sunlight

2. Susanne wants to write a description of the kitchen in her house. She wants to create an overall impression of the kitchen as a warm, cozy place to be on a winter's afternoon.

dirty dishes stacked in the sink   sunlight pouring through the window
noisy, as people come and go   smell of muffins baking

B. Write another detail that could be included in both Raymond's and Susanne's descriptions. (Answers will vary.)

3. Raymond's description: _happy customers buying flowers_

4. Susanne's description: _candles on the table_

Writer's Resources:
The Encyclopedia

An **encyclopedia** is a set of books that contains information about many subjects. Encyclopedia articles give information about people, places, things and events.

- Each book, or volume, in the set has articles that are arranged in alphabetical order.

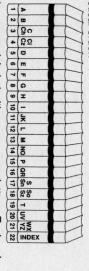

A	Ci	Ci																S	So		WX	
B	Ch	Cz	D	E	F	G	H	I	J K	L	M	N O	P	Q R	Sh	Sz	T	UV	YZ		INDEX
1	2	3	4	5	6	7	8	9	10 11	12	13	14 15	16	17 18	19	20	21	22			

- The volumes are labeled with one or more letters. Each volume includes subjects beginning with that letter.

Every encyclopedia has an **index** that lists all the subjects written about in the encyclopedia.

A. Circle the number of the encyclopedia volume that would contain information on each of the following subjects. Use the set of encyclopedias above.

1. Connecticut
   3   **(4)**   19

2. Eagles
   1   **(6)**   17

3. hockey
   (9)   11   15

4. Lake Michigan
   (12)   13   17

5. Ohio
   (9)   11   **(14)**

6. peanuts
   1   **(15)**   20

B. Match each animal name with the volume that would have an article on the subject. Draw a line between the name and the box that stands for the volume.

7. caribou
8. camel
9. chimpanzee

10. cougar
11. coyote
12. cheetah

| C–Ch |
| Ci–Cz |

What Is a Pronoun?

A **pronoun** is a word that takes the place of one or more nouns.

Singular Pronouns: I, you, he, she, it, me, him, her
Plural Pronouns: we, you, they, us, them

noun: The dogs are barking.   Give the dogs a biscuit.

pronoun: They are barking.   Give them a biscuit.

A. Circle the word **singular** if the underlined pronoun is singular. Circle the word **plural** if the underlined pronoun is plural.

1. I saw Leroy painting some pictures.   **singular**   plural

2. He gave them to his mother.   **singular**   plural

3. Mrs. Franklin, the art teacher, saw them.   singular   **plural**

4. She said that Leroy will be a great artist one day.   **singular**   plural

5. Leroy went with them to the art show.   singular   **plural**

B. Underline the pronoun in parentheses that correctly completes the second sentence. Use the underlined word or words as clues.

6. Last week Leroy painted a picture of his dog.
   (He, They) has painted many pictures of animals.

7. Greg and I watched Leroy paint one day.
   (Us, We) were very interested.

8. Greg asked Leroy for one of the pictures.
   Leroy gave (him, it) a picture of a lion.

9. Greg showed the picture to his parents.
   Leroy gave (him, it) a picture of a lion.

10. His parents even bought a frame for the picture.
    Greg hung (it, them) in his room.

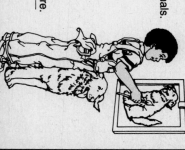

Subject Pronouns

A **subject pronoun** is a pronoun that is used as the subject of a sentence.

Subject Pronouns

Singular:	I, you, he, she, it
Plural:	we, you, they

Patty is here.   Chris and Don came late.
She is here.   They came late.

A. Underline the subject pronoun in each sentence.

1. Wanda is my sister. She is 15 years old.
2. I like to take hikes.
3. We often hike together.
4. You should come along some day.
5. Hiking is good exercise. It is fun, too.

B. Write the correct subject pronoun. Use the underlined word or words as clues.

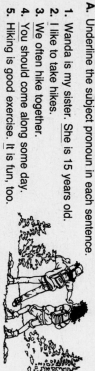

6. Last Saturday Dad wanted to go on a picnic. He _____ quickly packed the picnic basket.

7. Mom and I liked the idea. We _____ got out a map.

8. Mom found several interesting parks. She _____ finally chose one about 15 miles away.

9. At the park, forest rangers were riding on horses. They _____ were there to help people.

10. Mom, Dad, and I had a wonderful time that day. We _____ plan to have another picnic very soon.

Object Pronouns

An **object pronoun** is a pronoun that is used in the predicate of a sentence. It may follow an action verb or a word such as **in, into, to, with, for, by,** or **at.**

Object Pronouns

Singular:	me, you, him, her, it
Plural:	us, you, them

The children ate the raisins. The children ate them.

A. Underline the object pronoun in each sentence.

1. I like reading very much. Sometimes Mrs. Smith tells me to read aloud.
2. I think Bryan is the best reader. Mrs. Smith asks him to read often.
3. Mrs. Smith helps us with hard words.
4. Sometimes she describes different books. Then she gives them out.
5. Mrs. Smith is a wonderful teacher. The class likes her very much.

B. Complete each sentence with the correct object pronoun. Use the underlined word or words as clues.

6. Summer vacation begins soon for Wade and me. Our grandparents have invited us _____ to their home in Arizona.

7. Grandfather Frey flies a small airplane. We always ask him _____ for a ride.

8. I will have a birthday in Arizona. My grandparents might give me _____ a party.

9. We always have a wonderful time with our grandparents. We will send them _____ a thank-you letter.

Possessive Pronouns

A **possessive pronoun** shows who or what owns something. A possessive pronoun takes the place of one or more possessive nouns.

Possessive Pronouns

Singular: my, your, his, her, its
Plural: our, your, their

Cindy took swimming lessons.	Mother and Father drove Cindy to the pool.
<u>Her</u> teacher was very good.	<u>Their</u> car is getting old.

A. Underline the possessive pronoun in each sentence.

1. I took swimming lessons last summer. <u>My</u> lessons lasted for six weeks.

2. Miss Davis was the teacher. <u>Her</u> first <u>name</u> was Susie.

3. There were six other children <u>in</u> the class. <u>Their</u> parents watched the lessons.

4. Lance Hodges was in the class. <u>His</u> father is the police chief.

5. Have you ever taken swimming <u>lessons</u>? <u>Your</u> swimming would improve with lessons.

B. Write the correct possessive pronoun. Use the underlined word or words as clues.

6. Once I tried to swim in the ocean. That was the summer _____ my _____ family went to Cape Cod.

7. First my brother Jack jumped into the water. He yelled when the cold water hit _____ his _____ body.

8. Jack and I hated the ocean's salty taste. _____ Our _____ parents didn't seem to mind it.

9. Mom and Dad floated on top of the water. _____ Their _____ bodies bobbed up and down.

Using I and me Correctly

I → Use in the subject of a sentence.	<u>I</u> collect stamps. <u>Me</u> collect stamps.
me → Use after an action verb or words such as **in, into, with, by, or at.**	Dad tells <u>me</u> about stamps. Dad tells X about stamps.

A. Underline the correct word in parentheses.

1. (I, me) have collected many interesting stamps.

2. Dad helps (I, me) with the stamps.

3. He always gives (I, me) good advice.

4. What he knows about stamps always surprises (I, <u>me</u>).

5. Tomorrow (I, me) will buy four new stamps.

B. Write the word **I** or **me** to complete each sentence.

6. _____ I _____ joined a stamp club.

7. My friend Eric invited _____ me _____ to a meeting.

8. Stamps interest _____ me _____ a lot.

9. _____ I _____ took my stamp books to the meeting.

10. Eric introduced _____ me _____ to everyone.

11. _____ I _____ traded stamps with one member.

12. _____ I _____ gave her a one-cent stamp.

13. She gave _____ me _____ a two-cent stamp.

14. _____ I _____ had a wonderful time at the meeting.

15. Eric will call _____ me _____ for the next meeting.

Mechanics: Pronoun
Contractions

A **contraction** is a word made up of two words.

I am	→ I'm	we are	→ we're
they will	→ they'll	you have	→ you've
she is	→ she's	he had	→ he'd
she has	→ she's	he would	→ he'd

An **apostrophe** (') shows that one or more letters are missing.

I will → I wi̲l̲l̲ → I wi ll → I ['] ll → I'll

A. Underline each contraction. Then write the two words that make up the contraction.

1. I'm glad it is a sunny day. _____ I am
2. We're wasting time. _____ We are
3. She's got a good idea. _____ She has
4. They'll like it a lot. _____ They will
5. You've never played basketball in the park? _____ You have
6. I'll be a forward. _____ I will
7. He'd be a good guard. _____ He would
8. They'll have enough players for a second team. _____ They will
9. He'd rather be on that team. _____ He would
10. We're having a great time! _____ We are

B. Underline each pair of words that could be a contraction. Then write the contraction.

11. She has left her lunch under her desk. _____ She's
12. I will take it to her. _____ I'll
13. She will be thankful. _____ She'll
14. You are a thoughtful person. _____ You're
15. I am glad I could help. _____ I'm

Vocabulary Building:
Homophones and Homographs

Homophones are words that sound the same but have different spellings and meanings.

week—not strong **week**—seven days
I'm too weak to lift that box. I'll call you in a week.

Homographs are words that are spelled the same but have different meanings. Some homographs also have different pronunciations.

lead (pronounced led) a metal **lead** (pronounced lēd) to guide
This lead pipe weighs a lot. Will you lead us to the stables?

A. Underline the correct word in parentheses.

1. A (knew, new) student just came to our school.
2. (Their, There) are some things she didn't know about the school.
3. For example, one day she broke the (heel, heal) of her shoe.
4. One (piece, peace) of her shoe was on her foot and the other was in her hand.
5. She asked (to, two) classmates what to do.
6. They (cent, sent) her to the art room.
7. If you (brake, break) anything, the art room is the place to go.
8. (It's, Its) on the main floor.
9. The girl didn't (waste, waist) any time.
10. Her shoe (seems, seams) to be all right now.

B. Write the word from the box that correctly completes the sentence.

post	present	palm

11. In what states do _____ palm _____ trees grow?
12. We should _____ post _____ this picture on the bulletin board.
13. I had to return one _____ present _____ I got for my birthday.
14. The boy placed the coins in the _____ palm _____ of his hand.
15. Who will _____ present _____ the awards for the best costume?

Grammar and Writing Connection: Combining Sentences

RETEACHING·75

When you combine two or more sentences, you may list several words in a row. This list is called a **series**.

- Place the word **and** or **or** before the last word in a series.
- Words in a series are separated by commas.

Sometimes you can combine sentences by adding words in a series.

Markers	were in the art room.
Paints	were in the art room.
Brushes	were in the art room.

| Markers, | paints, | and | brushes |
were in the art room.

Combine these groups of sentences by joining words in a series.

1. Mrs. Miller helped Tod.
Mrs. Miller helped David.
Mrs. Miller helped Louis.

Mrs. Miller helped Tod, David, and Louis.

2. Did David use red?
Did David use blue?
Did David use white?

Did David use red, blue, or white?

3. Horses were in Tod's picture.
Cows were in Tod's picture.
Pigs were in Tod's picture.

Horses, cows, and pigs were in Tod's picture.

4. Old photographs were on Louis's poster.
Magazine pictures were on Louis's poster.
Drawings were on Louis's poster.

Old photographs, magazine pictures, and drawings were on Louis's poster.

Group Writing: A Persuasive Paragraph

RETEACHING·76

The **purpose** of a persuasive paragraph is to **convince an audience** to feel the way the writer does.

- Opinions stated clearly ———→ The topic sentence usually states the opinion.

- Order of reasons ———————→ Reasons that support the opinion follow, with the most important reasons given first.

- Facts that support the opinions —→ Back up the opinion with facts. Facts help persuade the audience that the opinion is sound.

A. State your opinion about each of the following topics. Write your opinion in the form of a topic sentence for a persuasive paragraph. (Answers will vary.)

1. television _____ There are not enough good programs for children.

2. movies _____ There should be more movies for family viewing.

B. Read the following persuasive paragraph. Then answer the questions.

Bicycle riders should have to wear helmets. Helmets would prevent minor head injuries. They would also prevent more serious head injuries, which are sometimes fatal. The number of injured motorcycle riders fell sharply when they had to wear helmets. If bicycle riders had to wear helmets, the number of injured bicycle riders would also fall.

3. What is the writer's opinion? _____ Bicycle riders should have to wear helmets.

4. What is the first reason given to support that opinion? _____ Helmets would prevent minor head injuries.

5. What is a fact given to support the opinion? _____ The number of injured motorcycle riders fell sharply when they had to wear helmets.

6. Did this persuasive paragraph make you agree with the writer? Explain why or why not. _____ Answers will vary.

Name

Thinking and Writing:
Telling Fact from Opinion

A **fact** is a statement that can be proved or checked.
An **opinion** is something that is believed. It cannot be proved or checked.

A. Write **fact** if the statement is a fact or **opinion** if the statement is an opinion.

1. I think that everyone should get involved in a sport. _____ opinion

2. Baseball is a sport in which you play on a team. _____ fact

3. In tennis, there are either two or four players. _____ fact

4. Football is more fun to play than soccer. _____ opinion

5. In a basketball game, points are scored when the ball goes into the net. _____ fact

6. People who play ice hockey must know how to skate. _____ fact

7. You will enjoy sports more if you have a favorite team that you can watch play. _____ opinion

B. What is your opinion about sports? Do you have a favorite team? Why do you like this particular sport or team?

8. Write your opinion about sports. Write it in the form of a topic sentence for a persuasive paragraph. (Answers will vary.)

_____

9. Write one fact to support your topic sentence. _____

10. Write one opinion to support your topic sentence. _____

Name

Writer's Resources: The Atlas
and the Almanac

An **atlas** is a book of maps. It usually contains several kinds of maps for one area.
An **almanac** gives facts about populations, current events, famous people, sports, elections, and many other subjects. A new almanac is published every year. It provides up-to-date information.

Circle **atlas** or **almanac** to tell where you would find the answer to each question.

1. What United States city has the largest population? (almanac) atlas

2. Where is the capital of Spain located? almanac (atlas)

3. On which of the Hawaiian Islands is Honolulu located? almanac (atlas)

4. What are the abbreviations for all the states? (almanac) atlas

5. Who is the president of Ireland? (almanac) atlas

6. What should you do if someone is choking? (almanac) atlas

7. Is Greece closer to Turkey or to Switzerland? almanac (atlas)

8. In what ocean is the island of Madagascar? almanac (atlas)

9. What state is directly north of Nebraska? almanac (atlas)

10. In what state is Bennett College located? almanac (atlas)

11. What was the population of the United States in 1610? (almanac) atlas

12. Who won the Grammy Awards last year? (almanac) atlas

13. What is Pearl Buck known for? (almanac) atlas

14. What is the largest lake in Nevada? almanac (atlas)

15. What is the closest Canadian province to Prince Edward Island? almanac (atlas)

T39

What Is an Adverb?

An **adverb** is a word that tells more about a verb.

An adverb tells **when** an action takes place.

where	
I happily go to camp. →	tells **how**
I never miss camp. →	tells **when**
My cabin is there. →	tells **where**

Many adverbs end with **ly**.

A. Underline each adverb.

1. Come inside with me.
2. My bunk is here.
3. Sometimes I listen to the crickets.
4. Crickets live everywhere.
5. The crickets call loudly to one another.

B. Underline each adverb. Then write the verb that each adverb describes.

6. Soon I fall asleep. _____ fall
7. Then the bugle plays. _____ plays
8. It easily wakes us. _____ wakes
9. I always make my bed. _____ make
10. We rush outside for roll call. _____ rush
11. Suddenly rain begins. _____ begins
12. Rain rarely falls. _____ falls
13. The counselors quickly cancel all outdoor activities. _____ cancel
14. We eat breakfast slowly. _____ eat
15. That day lasted forever. _____ lasted

More About Adverbs

An **adverb** is a word that tells more about a verb. It tells **how, when,** or **where.** An adverb can be put at the beginning of a sentence, before or after the verb, or at the end of a sentence. If you use an adverb to begin a sentence, place a comma after it.

Slowly, Tom walked to school.
Tom walked slowly to school.
Tom slowly walked to school.
Tom walked to school slowly.

A. Circle the question that each underlined adverb answers.

1. I really enjoy puzzles. where when (how)
2. There is the hardest puzzle! (where) when how
3. I work on the puzzles regularly. where (when) how
4. I often do a puzzle instead of watching TV. where (when) how
5. I work here. (where) when how
6. This lamp shines brightly. where when (how)
7. Sometimes, my father helps me. where (when) how
8. He works carefully. where when (how)
9. I have completed another puzzle successfully. where when (how)
10. Each piece fits perfectly. where when (how)

B. Write the correct word in parentheses.

11. I (easy, easily) find the border pieces. _____ easily
12. (Slow, Slowly), the puzzle takes shape. _____ Slowly
13. The face of the dog can be seen (clearly, clear). _____ clearly
14. (Quick, Quickly), I find the missing pieces. _____ Quickly
15. I (happy, happily) place the last piece. _____ happily

Using Adverbs to Compare

RETEACHING·81

An **adverb** can be used to make comparisons.

Short adverbs:

- Add **er** to compare two actions.
  This horse jumped <u>higher</u> than that horse.
- Add **est** to compare more than two actions.
  Of all the horses in the contest, this one jumped the <u>highest</u>.

The words **more** and **most** are usually used to form comparisons with adverbs that end in **ly** and with longer adverbs.

- Use **more** to compare two actions.
  This horse ran <u>more quickly</u> than that horse.
- Use **most** to compare more than two actions.
  Of all the horses in the contest, this one ran the <u>most quickly</u>.

Underline the word or words in parentheses that correctly complete each sentence.

1. Of all local events, our county fair is the (more enjoyable, <u>most enjoyable</u>).

2. I arrived at the fair (earlier, <u>earliest</u>) than my friend Jeb.

3. Last year Mr. Jenson's pig ate (<u>more quickly</u>, most quickly) than Jeb's pig.

4. Of all the other children, I usually cut the wool off my sheep the (more neatly, <u>most neatly</u>).

5. The person who cuts the wool off the (more quickly, <u>most quickly</u>) is the winner.

6. Last year I cut (faster, <u>fastest</u>) than Jeb.

7. In one contest, the pet frog that reaches the finish line the (<u>sooner</u>, soonest) wins a prize.

8. Of all the frogs in that contest, my frog jumped the (more swiftly, <u>most swiftly</u>).

9. My dad's workhorse won a prize by pulling the (harder, <u>hardest</u>) of all the horses.

Using good and well Correctly

RETEACHING·82

Good is an adjective. It describes a noun.
It may come before a noun. → That was <u>good</u> food.
It may follow a linking verb. → That food was <u>good</u>.

Well is usually an adverb. It tells more about a verb.
My mother cooks <u>well</u>.

A. Underline the correct word in parentheses.

1. This science-fiction book is (<u>good</u>, well).
2. Stories about the future are always (good, <u>well</u>).
3. Of course, the action has to be written (good, <u>well</u>).
4. Then I can imagine the story (good, <u>well</u>).
5. To me, (<u>good</u>, well) books are better than movies.

B. Write **good** or **well** to complete each sentence.

6. These are ____ good ____ sneakers.

7. They help me run ____ well ____.

8. There is ____ good ____ padding in the bottom.

9. The softness is ____ good ____ for my feet.

10. The sneakers wear ____ well ____.

11. The laces work ____ well ____.

12. White is a ____ good ____ color for sneakers.

13. These sneakers are ____ good ____ for both walking and running.

14. Exercise is important for ____ good ____ health.

15. With these sneakers I should do ____ well ____ in all sports.

Negatives

Some sentences include the word **no,** or other words that mean "no." These words are called **negatives.** Some negatives contain *no.*

Negatives →	no	none	no one	nowhere
	not	never	nobody	nothing
	Others include the contraction **n't.**

Never use two negatives in a sentence. → I didn't see *no one.*
Change one of the negatives without   I didn't see *anyone.*
changing the meaning of the sentence. → I saw *no one.*

A. Underline the word that correctly completes each sentence.

1. I won't (never, ever) go to a scary movie again.
2. I couldn't look at (none, any) of the monsters.
3. There wasn't (anywhere, nowhere) for me to go except the lobby.
4. I didn't like (any, none) of the special effects.
5. I can't find (one, no) good thing to say about scary movies.

B. Rewrite each incorrect sentence. Substitute a positive word for one negative word. (Answers will vary.)

6. Isn't no one going to help me with this puzzle?
   Isn't anyone going to help me with this puzzle?

7. I can't even find nobody to collect all the pieces.
   I can't even find anybody to collect all the pieces.

8. There's a corner piece that I can't find nowhere.
   There's a corner piece that I can't find anywhere.

9. I shouldn't have never started this puzzle.
   I shouldn't have ever started this puzzle.

10. This isn't no way to have fun.
    This isn't any way to have fun.

Mechanics: Punctuating Titles

When you write, you may need to name a book or story that you have read. When you write titles, there are certain rules to follow.

• The first, last, and all important words in a title should be capitalized.
   The Wonderful Wizard of Oz

• Underline titles of books, magazines, and newspapers.

Books →	**The Case of the Missing Clock**
Newspapers →	**Chicago Tribune**
Magazines →	**Reader's Digest**

• Use quotation marks to punctuate titles of articles, stories, songs, and poems.

Article →	"Watching Whales"
Story →	"Killer Whale"
Song →	"Three Jolly Fishermen"
Poem →	"Where Go the Boats"

Circle the title in parentheses that is written correctly.

1. I have just finished reading the book (Myths and Folklore, Myths and Folklore).

2. I have a subscription to the magazine (Young Athlete, Young Athlete).

3. The local newspaper, the (Warren Newsbeat, Warren Newsbeat), prints the scores of the Little League games.

4. (Animal Atlas of the World, Animal Atlas of the World) is a very interesting book.

5. Mom just read an article called ("Fun Things for Rainy Days," Fun Things for Rainy Days).

6. The (New York Times, new york times) is one of the biggest newspapers in the United States.

7. She read the story (Frog in The Pond, "Frog in the Pond").

Name _____

Vocabulary Building: Borrowed Words

The English language has many words that come from other languages.

Borrowed words —⌐ are words that come from other languages.
⌐ are words that became part of our own language with time.

(Spanish) guitarra ——→ (English) guitar

A dictionary often will tell you from which language a borrowed word comes.

Use each borrowed word in a sentence. If a word is unfamiliar, look up its meaning in a dictionary. (Answers will vary.)

1. (American Indian) pecan ___ Mom made a delicious pecan pie. ___

2. (Spanish) tornado ___ The tornado destroyed many homes. ___

3. (French) prairie ___ In the Old West, people crossed the prairie in wagon trains. ___

4. (Portuguese) zebra ___ Is a zebra black with white stripes or white with black stripes? ___

5. (German) frankfurter ___ I want my frankfurter on a roll with mustard. ___

6. (Italian) macaroni ___ For lunch we had macaroni and cheese and a salad. ___

7. (Latin) video ___ Have you seen the new video game at the mall? ___

Name _____

Grammar and Writing Connection: Combining Sentences

When you use words and phrases in your own writing that tell **how**, **where**, or **when**, look for ways to combine sentences that have similar ideas.

Our dog Morgan chases rabbits often. ——→ tells **when**
Our dog Morgan chases rabbits eagerly. ——→ tells **how**
Our dog Morgan chases rabbits outside. ——→ tells **where**
Our dog Morgan often chases rabbits eagerly in the backyard.

Write a word or phrase that answers the question in parentheses. Then combine the groups of sentences by joining words that tell **how**, **where**, or **when**. (Answers will vary.)

1. Morgan sees a rabbit.
He sees a rabbit (where?) ___ outside ___ .
Morgan sees a rabbit outside.

2. Morgan's tail points.
It points (where?) ___ up ___ .
Morgan's tail points up.

3. He chases the rabbit.
He chases it (how?) ___ fearlessly ___ .
He chases the rabbit fearlessly.

4. Morgan catches a rabbit.
(when?) ___ Occasionally ___ he catches one.
Occasionally Morgan catches a rabbit.

5. (How?) ___ Proudly ___ Morgan carries the rabbit.
He carries it (where?) ___ here ___ .
Proudly Morgan carries the rabbit here.

Group Writing:
A Research Report

The **purpose** of a research report is to give information to an **audience** about a specific topic.

- **Notetaking** → Taking notes will help you to remember what you have read. Write only main ideas and important details.
- **Outlining** → An **outline** helps you to organize a report. Use your notes to list items in the order in which you wish to discuss them.

Title

I. Main topic ————→ will be a paragraph
   A. Detail that supports the main topic ——→ subtopic
   B. Detail that supports the main topic ——→ subtopic

- **Organizing Information Logically** → A research report should be organized in a logical manner so that the reader can easily follow the ideas that you wish to present.

Here is the first part of an outline. Read it and answer the questions.

Superman

I. Powers of Superman
   A. Can fly very fast
   B. X-ray vision
   C. Super strength
   D. Super hearing

1. What is the main topic of this outline? ___ Powers of Superman
2. How many details support the main idea? ___ four
3. What is the last detail presented? ___ super hearing
4. What would the notes for this outline be about? ___ Superman's powers
5. If you were writing a report based on this part of the outline, how many paragraphs would you write? Explain your answer. ___ one paragraph because there should be one main idea in every paragraph

---

Thinking and Writing:
Summarizing

A **summary** tells the most important ideas of a longer piece of writing. A summary is short. It gives only the main idea and facts that the audience will need to know.

When you summarize information, ── keep your audience and
                                     purpose in mind.
                                     choose only those details that
                                     are the most important.

Write a three-sentence summary of this report for members of your science club. (Answers will vary.)

Animals' Tails

Tails are not just a nice addition that animals have and people don't. Tails have different purposes for different animals, but all of the purposes are important. For example, animals may use their tails to communicate, for warmth, for balance, for hanging, and for grabbing things.

When a dog sleeps, it curls its tail around itself to keep warm. However, when it wakes up, it will wag its tail to tell you it's happy. White-tailed deer also communicate with their tails. If there's danger, they raise their tails straight up like flags.

A kangaroo's tail is very important. Without it, a kangaroo couldn't keep its balance. Squirrels and monkeys also use their tails for balance. Cows, on the other hand, use their tails to push away pesty flies.

Tails are very important to animals. They have many different purposes like communicating, keeping the animal warm, balancing, grabbing, and hanging. For example, dogs use their tails for warmth when they sleep and to communicate when they are awake.

Name _____

Writer's Resources: Graphs, Tables, and Maps

Writers consult special resources to locate facts. Some possible resources are graphs, tables, and maps.

Graphs and **tables** are good ways of showing information about numbers.

Kinds of Pets Owned by Students
in Mrs. Ricker's Class

Number of Students				
8				
6				
4				
2				
0				
	Cats	Dogs	Hamsters	

Kinds of Pets Owned by Students
at Emerson Elementary School

PETS	BOYS	GIRLS	TOTAL
Dogs	56	33	89
Cats	64	81	145
Hamsters	8	2	10

Maps also give facts. They show where things are and how far one place is from another.

BRIDGE TOWN

Washington St.

Parking Lot	Bike Shop		Mrs. Smith's house		Mrs. Ricker's house	Library

Emerson Drive

| Book Store | Pet Shop | Park | Grocery Store | Mrs. Elliot's house |

Main Street

Park Avenue

Emerson Elementary School

Mrs. Wilson's house

Madison Road

N
W — E
S

Use the graph, table, or map to answer the following questions.

1. How many students own dogs in Mrs. Ricker's class? ___seven___

2. Which pet do the fewest number of students in Mrs. Ricker's class have? ___hamsters___

3. What is the most popular pet at Emerson Elementary School? ___cat___

4. How many boys own dogs at Emerson Elementary School? ___56___

5. When you leave the pet shop, do you go north or south to the school? ___north___